March birthd
from Grand

WINGED CANOES AT NOOTKA

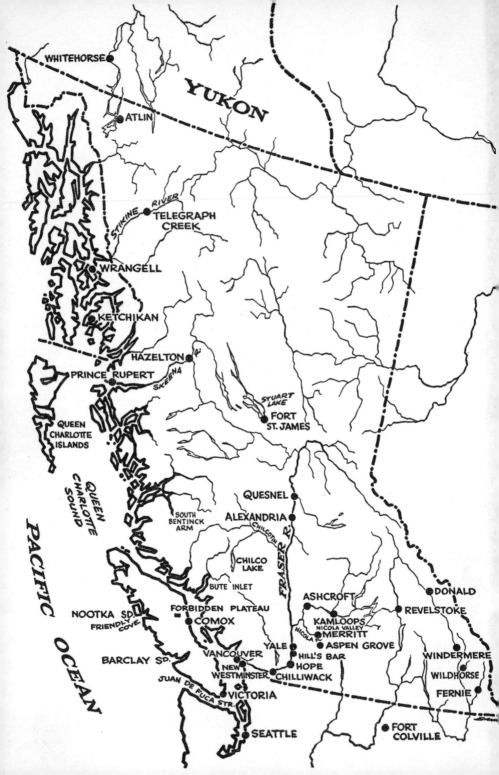

WINGED CANOES
AT NOOTKA

and

OTHER STORIES OF THE EVERGREEN COAST

By

Pamela Stephen

Illustrations by Annora Brown

J. M. Dent & Sons (Canada) Limited

Toronto   Vancouver

DEDICATION

❦

To the Memory of
RICHARD NOEL CRUIT, *R.C.A.F.*,
My Son,
Killed in Action in Tunisia,
November 28, 1942.
Age 19 years.

FOREWORD

In the pages which follow I have taken an informal approach to the early history of British Columbia. This collection is comprised of tales, each covering some episode in the years from Cook's landing at Nootka Sound up to the First World War. It is hoped that they move forward as would the scenes in a pageant, briefly picturing some of the highlights of the past.

All of these stories are founded on fact. Some few of them follow closely the available records. In others I have permitted my imagination to take over and have used fictitious names and incidents to weave a tale around the facts. Still others come from the lips of oldtimers and appear in print for the first time.

In many instances I have taken liberties with the technique of the modern short story. I felt this to be necessary in order to give a more complete picture of the period in question or the lives of the people involved.

This book is offered in the hope that it may awaken in old and young alike a greater interest in our past and an awareness of the romance which marked the early days of British Columbia.

A number of these stories in their original form were broadcast over the air on my radio program, sponsored by the British Columbia Parent-Teacher Federation. It was the warm response to these broadcasts which encouraged me to expand the series and offer them in book form.

I am deeply grateful to Mr. T. W. Woodhead, to Mrs. Ladler and Miss Isobel McTavish of the Boys' and Girls' Department of the Vancouver Public Library, who read my manuscript and kindly offered their opinions; Miss Dorothy Taylor, Publisher of the British Columbian, New Westminster; Miss Madge Wolfenden and members of the staff of the Provincial Archives, Victoria; and to Doctor Donalda Dickie whose "protégé" I became at an early stage in my writing and whose criticisms and encouragement have sustained me through my struggles.

PAMELA STEPHEN.

Contents

CONTENTS—Continued

Winged Canoes at Nootka

Captain Cook Arrives at Vancouver Island

Rain drummed mournfully against cedar roofs in the Indian village at Nootka on the west coast of Vancouver Island; yet this gloomy March day in 1778 was to live in the memory of every Nootkan Indian.

It started out with an event as depressing as the weather: the hunters returned empty-handed after a vain search for whales. The women, children and old men who crowded to the beach to welcome them all realized that this disappointment might mean hungry days ahead. The women tried to encourage their men as they followed them up the shale beach to the chief's huge lodge. The Nootkans were proud of their reputation as the only tribe on the coast who killed whales, and they depended on them for food and for trade with other tribes.

Inside the chief's lodge, the men squatted on the earthen floor around the blazing fire. The chief stepped down from his living quarters and joined them. He listened gravely as the harpooners told of searching the waters without sighting a single whale. While they talked the women hurried to prepare a meal, sending the children to play on the platforms which circled the great room. Smoke spiralled from the open fire and rose to escape in wisps through the shutter in the roof. A silence fell until suddenly a quavering voice called out,

"There is no need to be sad. Our people will have plenty to eat, and soon great honour comes to Nootka."

Everyone turned to look at the speaker, an old man who stood shaking with excitement. His frail body seemed to have regained strength as he hurried across the room to stand before his chief.

"I have had word from the Great Ones," he said. "My helpers have told me where the whales have gone. They also told me that strange things will happen here. My helpers, the Great Ones, have given me back my medicine and I will be once more a great shaman among you." His old eyes looked around the room until they found the face of Komeka, the young shaman, who stared at him in contempt.

"Old Nekus dreams again," he said. "He sits by the fire and dozes, then tries to make us believe his dreams. His medicine is as weak as he is . . . if the Great Ones had a message for us, they would have revealed it to me, your shaman."

One of the hunters laughed. The others joined in until the room was filled with their mirth. Old Nekus looked about him bewildered as he realized that they had not believed him. He turned and walked away from that cruel laughter. The rain had stopped as he stumbled towards the beach where his small dug-out lay, drawn up high above the other canoes. He seldom used it now. He went to it and sat on the bow, thinking of the scene he had left. Suddenly his despair gave way to a wave of strange thoughts that flooded his mind as though a great voice had reached his ears.

"Nekus," it said, "go and find the whales where you were told they are waiting. When you return, lead the hunters to them. Then they will know it was not a dream you had. They will know your helpers are still with you and your medicine is strong. They said you were too old when they chose Komeka to fill your place as shaman. Now show them that they were wrong."

Old Nekus rose to his feet and nodded his head. Yes, this he must do. His breath came in gasps as he dragged the dugout into the water and picking up the paddle, started towards the mouth of the Sound. A strange feeling of power came over him and soon the dip of his paddle beat rythmically through the grey water. He was too deep in his thoughts at first to notice the thickening fog drifting towards him. When he did notice it he stopped paddling and looked about him. His sense of power left him and the bleak loneliness pressed down upon him. Must he turn back . . . admit defeat and have Komeka, the young shaman, laugh at him and say again that he was an old man who had dreamed of great medicine. No, it was true what he had told them in the chief's lodge. His helpers *had* returned to him. They had promised him great things. He would not stop until he found the whales. He would show Komeka that his medicine was indeed strong. Picking up the paddle he drove the canoe forward.

Suddenly the fog lifted and the old man stared ahead. What he saw made him drop his paddle and cry out in terror. A huge monster with great white wings was coming straight towards him. Nekus shut his eyes tight and called to his helpers. This was not a whale . . . he had not been led to the place where the whales were hiding from the hunters. This monster must come from the Evil One.

Nekus snatched up the paddle but his hands were trembling so that he could barely hold it. Curiosity finally overcame his fear and he looked at the huge object which was now directly above him. As he stared at it he realized that it was not a monster . . . nor was it the Evil One. It was a huge winged canoe! Strange creatures stood on it and as he sat, too amazed to move, a figure at the rail waved to him. It was a human being like himself. But its face was pale like the underside of a fish. It was a *man* old Nekus decided, one of a very strange tribe. He waved timidly and the stranger motioned to him, inviting him to come closer. Nekus shook his head and, hurriedly swinging his dug-out about, paddled furiously for home.

As he neared the shore his fears left him and a feeling of excitement took their place. He could hardly wait to spread the news of the strangers who had come to Nootka in their winged canoe. Presently he saw a second great winged monster, but he did not stop this time. He had seen enough to know that the spirits guarding him had spoken truly to him as he sat by the fire in the chief's lodge. Great events indeed were coming to Nootka and he, Nekus, had been chosen as the first to know about them. He must hurry to his village and tell his tribesmen what he had seen.

Meantime, Captain James Cook stood at the rail of his vessel, the *Resolution*, and turning to one of his men remarked, "That old native in the canoe seemed terrified when he saw us."

"He has probably never seen a sailing ship before, Sir."

"No, I suppose not. I hope his people are friendly. We need wood and supplies sorely; it has been a long, hard journey since we left the Sandwich Islands. These waters are not easy to navigate and the winds and fogs are treacherous."

"The men are over-joyed by the sight of land, sir," said the senior officer, joining them. "Those mountains with their covering of green trees make it seem to be a land of rich growth. There will be wood aplenty for repairing our two ships, fresh water too, I hope. By the way, the *Discovery* is not lagging behind, as you can see. She is clearing the fog bank just a short distance behind us."

"Yes, I have seen her. We will land tomorrow and a good thing too. But I have work to do on my charts as soon as we clear the entrance and find anchorage."

"What name will you give this Sound, sir?"

"I shall name it 'King George's Sound,' and yonder cove shall be 'Friendly Cove,' because I doubt not that the natives will be friendly. That old man seemed so indeed, although somewhat frightened." The others joined in his laughter.

The next few hours passed quickly as Jim Cook sat working at his charts. He finished and stared unseeingly at the papers in front of him. His thoughts turned to the purpose of this voyage, his second to this new continent of North America. He knew the eyes of the whole world were upon him, waiting the results of this expedition.

The purpose of the voyage was the century old, world wide search for a North West passage which would open a short route to the Orient. Explorers from all countries had searched in vain for that passage. Now he was determined to find it for his country. Two ships, the *Discovery* and *Resolution*, had been outfitted with the greatest care by his government, no expense had been spared, and he had been honoured with the command of this expedition.

The honour had come to him because of his outstanding record as a navigator. Years of struggle and hard work had brought him this reward. He thought now of the young boy, Jim Cook, born in a two-room cottage in the small village in Yorkshire, England. His father had been too poor to give him much in the way of an education. The struggle to clothe and feed a large family had been almost more than his parents could manage until Mr. Cook finally got a job as manager of a farm. Jim, his youngest son, had shown promise as a student and the man his father worked for had financed the boy's education.

Even at that Jim had to leave school when he was thirteen years old. He smiled now as he remembered all this and the desperate struggle that he had gone through to keep up his studies. He could not have done it had it not been for the kind interest of Miss Mary Walker. What a good friend she had been . . . . she had tutored him, and encouraged him when he first showed an interest in navigation. When work on the farm became too heavy for his father and brother, and he had to give up his studies to help them, Miss Mary's interest and encouragement had not ceased. Jim had been determined to learn all he could in whatever spare time he had and she helped him to do this. At last the day came when he could leave the farm and go to sea. He continued his studies with even greater enthusiasm and his determination to use his knowledge in exploring and charting new waters grew with the years.

When war broke out between France and England and the destiny of Canada was at stake, young Cook joined the British Navy. It was his charts of the St. Lawrence River which made possible the capture of Quebec and so insured his country's victory. Yes, thought Cook, as memories of the past flooded over him, he had been well rewarded for his struggles. He had succeeded so far on this voyage, though the goal was still before him. On this journey he had discovered the Sandwich Islands and claimed them in the name of his king. He had named them after the Earl of Sandwich.

His thoughts turned now to his wife and children at

home in England. It was nearly a year since he had seen them. How much longer would it be before he was once more at home with them? He smiled wryly as he thought of that young Jim Cook who had dreamed of one day setting out on a voyage such as this one. He had come a long way from the poverty of his youth. It was true also that loneliness and stern self-discipline had marked the road to the fulfilment of his boyhood dreams.

A knock at the door and a voice calling to him brought him back to the present. "The natives are circling us in their canoes; what are your orders, sir? Are we to let them board us?"

"Yes, Jones. But make sure that the chief and the men in his canoe come aboard first. I will be there to meet them. Of course we will take the usual precautions against possible hostility. However, I will attend to those orders."

A short time later Captain Cook stood at the rail of his ship and looked shorewards. The green-timbered hills reached down to the sprawling village above the shoreline. Canoes, filled with natives were pushing off from the beach. He looked down and saw a huge canoe which had just circled his ship. It was carved and painted with weird images of fish and birds and he surmised it belonged to the chief.

There was a man sitting aft holding the steering paddle in his hands and staring up at the white man. Cook recognized him as the old native who had appeared out of the fog when they arrived in the Sound. Then his attention was diverted to a tall native who stood up in the canoe and, gazing up at the captain, threw handfuls of white down feathers and of red clay onto the water. Jim Cook knew from his experience with native tribes that this was a symbol of friendship and welcome. Just then the man,

obviously the chief, started to sing and at the same time
shake the rattles, he now held in each hand, in time to the
rhythm of his song. The natives in the other canoes which
had now reached the ship began to chant, first low, then
louder and louder until their voices filled the air with the
deep notes of a ceremonial song of welcome.

When it ended, Captain Cook raised his arm and motioned
to the chief to come aboard with his men. The first thing
the Nootkan chief did after formal greetings had taken place
was to unfasten the handsome sea otter cloak he wore draped
around his body. He presented it to the Captain. Cook
understood the value of those rich, soft furs and immediately
gave an order to one of his men. The man returned a few
minutes later carrying one of the Captain's coats, bright brass
buttons flashing against the dark cloth. With a low bow
Captain Cook offered it to the chief whose face broke into a
dazzling smile as he accepted it. He wore it with great pride
during the rest of the white man's visit to Nootka.

Old Nekus, meantime, was shivering with delight as he
looked timidly about the deck where he had followed his
chief. He had been allowed to accompany the latter on
this visit to the strange canoe. He was no longer frightened
by it nor by the strange human beings walking around on
it. They were men all right but very different in speech,
manner and dress from his own people. He watched his
tribesmen crowding around some of the pale-faced men
who were holding up objects and pointing to the fur cloak
his chief had given to the white chief. Old Nekus understood as did the other natives, that these men wanted to
trade the glittering objects for furs. He saw one man holding
a bright, shining thing which held him spell-bound for a
moment. But he turned dejectedly away from its temptation
. . . . he had no furs to offer. He was too old to hunt.

With sagging shoulders he walked to the rail and looked over the water towards the village. He saw the chief's lodge with the huge, carved totem pole standing in front of it. He had no lodge now or totem pole, the family crest and symbol of tribal honour. He lived on the bounty of his chief. Yet his helpers had told him of these great events which had happened.

He heard his name called and turned to see his chief beckoning to him. He hurried over and stood waiting while the white man spoke to the chief. He stared in awe as the latter turned and held something out to him. It was the shining object he had seen and coveted a moment before. Now this stranger was offering it to him. But he shook his head and murmured, "I have no furs." The chief laughed, then told him to take it. The white man was giving it to him, said his chief, because he had been the first to welcome him on his arrival at Nootka.

Old Nekus smiled shyly as he reached out and took the gift. He looked up at the tall man who offered it and stared for a moment into the penetrating eyes smiling kindly at him. He did not notice the brown hair tied with a ribbon, but the pale face held his attention. He realized suddenly, that in every way except colour, this man's features resembled his own. This was indeed a man like himself, not a being from the other world. A kindly man too, the eyes told him, harsh sometimes, but fair. Nekus laughed happily as he held the treasure close and, gesturing excitedly, thanked the stranger.

That night the old Indian stood in front of his chief's lodge before entering. It was again raining as it had been that morning, but what a difference! The dreary sound of the downpour on the roof was drowned out by the laughter and songs of the tribesmen inside. They were celebrating this great occasion and all thoughts of the failure of the whale hunt were forgotten. Old Nekus stared up at the towering totem pole, carved with the crests of his chief's clan. He went over to it and walking up the few steps, opened a trap door which was the entrance to the lodge as well as the mouth of the carved figure which formed its base. Before he stepped down into the room he thought proudly, "I have no totem or lodge it is true, but I have great medicine now. This shiny one, given me by the pale chief will bring me many good things and my power will be great. I will tell the hunters tomorrow where they can find the whales and they will believe me. The pale one in the winged canoe has given me back my place among my people." He straightened his frail shoulders as he walked to the crowd seated around the blazing fire.

Anger flamed in the eyes of Komeka as Nekus approached; the young shaman turned away as the chief motioned the old man to the place of honour by his side. Nekus obeyed proudly and the others respectfully made room for him. The singing started again and, holding his treasure close, his quavering voice joined in the chorus.

Meantime, Jim Cook was staring at the dark ceiling of his cabin as he waited for sleep to come. It had been an eventful day and marked another success in his career. He smiled as thought of the old Indian who had been overcome with joy when he gave him the brass candlestick.

"That old man saw a sailing ship for the first time today but he also saw the beginning of a new era," he thought. "Many ships will follow us here: as the years pass this will mean many changes for these Indians."

The quiet of night fell over Nootka and brought to a close that historic day when the white man arrived on the Coast of British Columbia.

The Adventurous Bride

The First White Woman to Visit our Pacific Shores.

It all began one day in October, 1786, when a quiet wedding was held in a church at Ostend in Flanders. The father of the bride performed the ceremony which united Frances Hornby Trevor with Captain Charles William Barkley. The pretty, seventeen year old bride knew that she would follow her adoring twenty-three year old groom wherever his sea-faring life led him. But she did not know that her wedding journey aboard his ship would last well over a year. Nor did she realize then the important role she would play in the history of a place to become known as British Columbia. Her father, the Reverend John Trevor, must have had misgivings as he thought of the hard though adventurous life his young daughter was facing. No doubt his unease would have been increased had he known more about the venture the groom was embarking upon immediately after the wedding. Captain Barkley was sailing to the North Pacific Coast on a poaching expedition, a strange honeymoon indeed for a girl who had led a very sheltered life.

11

Her husband's ship, the *Imperial Eagle,* was a former
East Indiaman, the *Loudoun.* It had been re-christened
and was sailing under Austrian colours. There was a good
reason for changing the registration of this 400 ton, ship-
rigged vessel mounting twenty guns. At that time the South
Sea Company and the East India Company held a monopoly
of British trading rights in the Pacific. Charles Barkley
intended to ignore this monopoly and do a bit of free-
trading or poaching. The venture was secretly financed by
certain employees of the East India Company. Charles himself had invested heavily in this risky enterprise.

The bride was delighted with her quarters aboard her
husband's ship and the first few days of the journey passed
happily. Frances discovered a way to help pass the time
which proved a satisfaction to herself. Even more important,
it proved to be an invaluable document for those who
came after her. She kept a diary which has become of great
historical value.

The first hint of trouble came when her husband took
ill. He was suffering from rheumatic fever and the inexpe-
rienced Frances became frantic with worry. She nursed him
as best she could but her one desire was to reach a port
where Charles could get proper medical attention. In her
diary she tells of an added worry. "The unprincipled attention of the first mate, supported by the second mate, who,
being a lieutenant in His Majesty's Service ought to have
had more honour." But in spite of her youth she put both
men in their place and kept them there. She was almost
overcome with relief when San Salvador was sighted; they
would stay there she decided until her husband had recovered from his illness.

When they arrived in this port, the Portuguese authorities
glowered suspiciously at the heavily armed ship. However,

when they learned that it was a trading vessel bound for the Pacific Coast they became friendly.

The Governor, on hearing of Captain Barkley's illness, was most gracious. He and his wife showed sympathy and understanding and made the lonely girl feel quite at home with them. Indeed, as soon as her husband was well enough, they entertained her lavishly at Government House.

Frances wrote in her diary: "The Ladies spoke French which was a great relief to me who did not understand a word of Portuguese at that time." Later, she wrote of the time when her husband had fully recovered and they returned this hospitality aboard the *Imperial Eagle*.

"The Governor or Vice-Roy with his lady Donna Marie and his little daughter with a numerous Suite and Officers and attendants, came to a fete aboard the *Imperial Eagle*, in a spendid Barge, dressed, as it is called, in all the colours of the rainbow, the Yards Manned, a Salute fired and a handsome collation spread."

It was hard for Frances to leave these friends and their gay hospitality. When they sailed out of port she was again facing a hard, lonely life aboard her husband's ship; but she seems to have enjoyed the adventure and the new horizons each day offered.

It was June of the next year when they reached Nootka, their destination, almost nine years after Captain Cook. Frances Barkley saw the gloomy, forest-clad hills and rocky cliffs which seemed to offer an inhospitable welcome in contrast to sunny San Salvador. She stood at the rail as the *Imperial Eagle* drew into the Sound. They would drop anchor in Friendly Cove and soon know whether her husband's venture would fail or succeed. All depended on the reception they received from the natives and whether they would bring their furs to the trading ship. Frances' mind was filled with doubts as the ship moved steadily forward. Presently they were moored in the Cove and her husband joined her. "What are those odd craft?" she asked, pointing to the shoreline.

"They are Indian war canoes." Her husband smiled as he answered. "The natives make them from huge trees which they fell. Canoe-making is quite an art with these people. They can paddle them at a smart clip and travel great distances in them. It is their only means of transportation on this coast. But see, they are coming out to us. I hope it is to trade. I must make ready to greet them and, if I can, win their friendship." He turned and hurried away.

The first canoe reached the ship and she looked down into it. Her excitement ebbed as she saw the occupant; she drew back in distaste, murmuring, "What a filthy Indian!" The paddle dropped from the man's hand and he sat motionless staring up at her. He seemed unaware of his long, straggling hair, unkempt beard and greasy otter-skin robe. Frances started to turn away but something about his eyes caught and held her attention. Puzzled, she stared down into the upturned face then spoke aloud in amazement, "Why his eyes are blue."

"Whose eyes are blue?" She had not heard Charles approach and she turned to him.

"I thought all natives had black eyes . . . that one down there in the canoe has blue, blue eyes."

Her husband leaned over the rail then straightened, "As I live and breathe, it is a white man."

Captain Barkley immediately called out an order and soon a rope ladder was thrown over the side and the white man climbed aboard and joined them.

To their astonishment the stranger spoke in flawless English, saying,

"I am John McKay. May I welcome you to Nootka. Madam, please forgive me for staring at you so rudely when I saw you at the rail of the ship; I thought my eyes were playing me tricks. You are the first white woman I have seen in over a year. More important, you are the first one to visit these shores."

It was not until later that Frances Barkley understood fully the importance of that remark. At the time she was speechless with surprise; she was being welcomed, not by a native as she had expected, but by a white man.

In the captain's quarters a short time later, McKay told them his story. He had come to Nootka on Captain Strange's trading brig, the *Captain Cook*, acting as surgeon. James Strange had conceived the idea of leaving someone at Nootka when he sailed away, who would win the native's friendship, and so ensure for him their trade in the valuable furs so many traders were beginning to desire. He had persuaded Dr. McKay to stay and live with the chief, promising to return for him in a year. The year passed and Strange did not keep his promise. At first John had been too interested in his surroundings to worry about his isolation. The powerful chief and his tribesmen had grown to like and respect him. Still, it had been a hard life. The supplies and clothing left with him had gone, some through use, some to the Indians. He had been forced finally to live on their bounty as a native. His medical knowledge had been useful . . . as long as he did not interfere with the medicine man or shaman. As time passed and Strange did not return McKay began to feel the seriousness of his situation. He was beginning to despair of ever getting away from Nootka. He was overjoyed when he sighted the *Imperial Eagle* and could barely restrain his anxiety to board her.

John looked at Mrs. Barkley as he said, "You indeed

thought I was a native. Your look of disgust showed me what I have become. I assure you, madam, it was necessity not choice." He joined in Captain Barkley's laughter at his wife's confusion.

They were interrupted by a member of the crew who hurried into the cabin to say that the Indians were flocking out to the ship in their canoes. When they reached the deck they saw a huge crowd of natives, some already climbing over the rail. They were talking excitedly in their native tongue.

When they saw Frances Barkley they stopped and an awed silence spread through the group. Their faces were immobile as they stared at her. She turned to John McKay and asked:

"Why do they stare so at me?"

"You forget, madam, they have never before seen a white woman. They wonder if you are not a supernatural being." He looked down at the deck as he added, "I am afraid I have told them too many tales about our ladies. But I told them the truth when I said our ladies were fair as the lilies, with cheeks like roses. You are a marvel of fairness to them. I am happy that they know now I did not lie."

The tension among the natives was broken when a bold warrior sidled up to the young girl and touched her arm. He turned to the others and jabbered excitedly. It took Dr. McKay's firm command to keep them all from touching her. They crowded around her, talking loudly all the while to the Doctor. He answered them in their own language then turned to the captain. "They will bring their finest furs to you if your wife will speak to them."

Startled, Frances was silent for a moment then as her husband nodded re-assuringly, she said, "I should like to meet your women and children." John translated this and the natives smiled happily as they listened.

It was not long before the canoes left for the village. The next day they returned, laden with furs. However, they did not give them in return for the privilege of hearing the voice of the captain's fair bride. They were paid in copper and trade goods. When the trading was over they invited the Barkleys ashore as their chief's guests.

The days passed swiftly and Frances enjoyed the exciting, new experiences she had with the Indians. The women's weaving of rushes and strands of cedar bark into robes, hats, baskets and other household articles amazed and fascinated her. The children seemed happy, like healthy little animals, though lacking in cleanliness by her standards. She saw them return from picking berries, which their mothers used for cooking or for extracting juices for dyes to be used in their household arts. There were so many new and interesting things to see and learn that she almost regretted the day when they left Nootka.

But that day was a happy one for Captain Barkley. His venture had succeeded beyond his highest hopes. The hold of the *Imperial Eagle* was filled to overflowing with hundreds of the finest sea-otter pelts. Indeed, he fully realized that he had John McKay to thank for this; it was his knowledge of the Nootkans' language and customs which made him invaluable as a trader. John, on the other hand, was overjoyed when he sailed away with his new friends, the Barkleys.

They had left Nootka behind them and were proceeding south along the coast of Vancouver Island when they reached an inlet. Captain Barkley named this after himself, Barkley Sound. In her diary Frances speaks of the places named by her husband.

"There was Frances Island, after myself; Hornby peak, also after myself; Cape Beale after our purser; Williams point and a variety of other names, all of which were familiar to us."

It was a lovely July day when an unexpected event added to the success of their voyage. Frances was on deck watching the forest-clad land when her husband joined her. They stood in silence as they watched the serene majesty of water and land. The silence was broken by her husband's sudden shout of excitement as he pointed ahead. His wife caught the words: "There it is! Captain Cook missed it." This historic moment is given in her own words in her diary:

"In the afternoon, to our great astonishment, we arrived off a large opening extending to the eastward, the entrance of which appeared to be about four leagues wide, and remained about that width as far as the eye could see, with a clear westerly horizon, which my husband immediately recognized as the long lost strait of Juan de Fuca, and to which he gave the name of the original discoverer, my husband placing it on his chart."

She refers here, of course, to the Greek navigator of the 16th. century, Juan de Fuca, who claimed to have sailed for more than twenty days on a strait which led from the Pacific to the Atlantic; the much sought-after Strait of Anian.

They sailed a few miles further south, past Cape Flattery, until they reached a small island off the steep bluffs of the Olympic Peninsula near which a small stream flowed into the ocean. It was here a note of tragedy entered the picture. Captain Barkley sent a boat crew of five men to get fresh water. They did not return and upon investigation it was discovered that they had been killed by hostile Indians.

The captain named the island, Destruction Island, and the stream, Destruction River.

Their final objective, the sale of the furs, was reached when they crossed the Pacific and entered the port of Macao in December, 1787. Here they found a good market for the rich cargo in the hold of the ship. The visit to the China coast with its ancient civilization fascinated Frances who during her long wedding voyage had seen a world of vast contrasts.

Frances Barkley's life was one of adventurous wanderings by the side of her sea-faring husband. She died at the age of seventy-two.

The story of the pretty bride who was the first white woman to visit the shores of what is now British Columbia is worthy of an important place in the annals of this Province.

Treachery at Friendly Cove

The Story of Martinez and Colnett.

The sun sparkled on the quiet waters of Friendly Cove one early summer day in 1789. The Indian village which had seemed so sleepy and still suddenly sprang into activity. Chief Callicum made his way down to the beach where an excited crowd was talking and pointing to the water beyond the Sound. He saw the cause of their excitement and smiled to himself. Another ship was coming into Nootka and his tribesmen were eager to board her and trade sea-otter skins for tools and trinkets.

Many ships had come to Nootka since that day in 1778 when Captain Cook first sailed into the harbour. They were English, American or Spanish, and the Indians were becoming accustomed to the white men. Chief Callicum had some good friends amongst the English seamen. Captain Meares was one, and another was a young man who had come with Captain Cook. Chief Callicum often wondered if he would see this young man again.

The Spaniards had been the first to build a settlement at Friendly Cove. A premonition of grave trouble came to

the Chief as he glanced up at the cliff where the Spanish
fort stood. Soldiers manned this fort and guns pointed
towards the native village. Chief Callicum and his people
had watched the commander of the fort, Captain Martinez,
giving orders to his men, whose subservient obedience had
suggested that he was a hard, stern man. The Indians had
been restless and uneasy since the day, three months ago,
when two Spanish war-ships, the *Princessa* and the *San
Carlos*, dropped anchor in Friendly Cove. The dark-skinned
men aboard them had lost no time in establishing themselves at Nootka. The flag of Spain flew over their fort.
What this meant the Nootkans did not know. Now, as
Chief Callicum watched the ship in full sail coming towards
the Sound, he sighed and wished it could be bringing
Captain Meares or that young man Colnett. Either would
be welcome.

By a strange circumstance it was indeed Captain Colnett
who was coming in towards Friendly Cove aboard the
Argonaut. Captain Meares had sent him to build a fur-
trading post on the land Meares had acquired from Chief
Maquinna on his last visit to Nootka. The *Argonaut* carried
supplies to last three years as well as tools and other building
materials. Colnett intended to build up a fur-trade with the
Indians of the coast and send a shipment of furs each year to
China's rich markets. The company which had sent him out
to command this enterprise was headed by Captain Meares
and his associates and was known as the *Associated Merchants
of London and India.*

But Chief Callicum did not know all this as he stood on
the beach and watched the ship near the Sound. A worried
look came into the eyes of the kindly, dignified chief as
he caught sight of Captain Martinez. The Spaniard had also
seen the vessel and stood watching it. When it was close to

the Sound he jumped into a small boat and started off for the *Princessa*. There, he hurried to the bow of his ship and looked across the water. An angry glint came into his eyes when he recognized the English flag at the mast of the *Argonaut*. But soon a cunning smile replaced that anger. He had already made up his mind what he was going to do.

Captain Colnett was unprepared for the sight of the two Spanish ships in the harbour. How would their presence affect his plans? He had little time to think however, before Captain Martinez boarded his ship, the *Argonaut*. The Spaniard's manner was courteous as he welcomed the Englishman to Friendly Cove. He suggested that Captain Colnett lose no time in mooring his ship beside the *Princessa*.

He added quickly that he was desperately in need of supplies which he was sure Captain Colnett could spare him. The bluff, out-spoken Colnett hesitated a moment, then said, "Of course, if you are in desperate need of anything I can spare you, but . . ."

He had no time to finish before Don Martinez suavely broke in,

"And you will do me the honour of dining with me to-night aboard my ship, no?"

"Well, perhaps I should wait until . . ." Captain Colnett started to reply but again he was interrupted.

"Please! We can discuss everything then and it will be so good to have a new face among us. You will have much to tell us of your plans. We grow tired, my officers and I, of the same subjects of conversation. Then it is agreed . . . until to-night, adios."

The Spaniard was gone before the Englishman could respond. Captain Colnett remained on deck after his guest left the ship. He felt a grave alarm as he stared at the garrison on the cliff. His eye caught the Spanish flag flying above the fort and he stared at it. A chill foreboding held him. He was startled when he looked down at the ship's side and saw a canoe. A bearded white man in the canoe called urgently, "Quick, quick, get me aboard."

At Colnett's command a ladder was lowered and the visitor scrambled aboard. He poured out a strange story to the Captain.

He had been one of the crew of the vessel *North West America,* which Captain Meares had built at Nootka on his last visit. When Meares left, this staunch little vessel had started its voyages to native villages along the coast, picking up furs from the traders. Immediately after his arrival the Spaniard, Martinez, had seized the post built by Meares' men and the *North West America* as well. All the Englishmen were held as prisoners although for the time being they were allowed to live at large. Martinez had told the Captain of the *North West America* that he had left Spanish headquarters in Mexico with orders to claim this territory for his country and establish a monopoly of the fur-trade. The haughty Spaniard was determined to break the hold on trade with the Indians which English seamen had established and prevent them from getting a foothold at Nootka. He would stop at nothing to gain these ends. Captain Colnett's informant went on to warn him against accepting Martinez' invitation to moor his ship inside the harbour. He advised him to turn about and sail away.

Colnett refused to be frightened by the situation, serious as it was. He could not sail away until he got a supply of fresh water and fish; the long voyage across the Pacific had almost depleted his stores. He frowned in perplexity as he tried to make a decision. Meantime, the man who had risked so much to warn him, hurried down to his canoe and slipped away.

After a great deal of grave thought Colnett decided to stay only long enough to give Martinez what he needed in return for a supply of his own needs. He would sail in the morning.

That night he boarded the *Princessa* and was received with such lavish hospitality and friendliness that his suspicions were lulled. Martinez assured him on his word of honour that he was free to sail at any time. The evening passed pleasantly and Colnett returned to his ship in a happier frame of mind.

The next day brought a sad change. The business of transferring supplies took Colnett once more to the *Princessa*. This time his reception was quite different. The Spaniard's manner was arrogant. He forced an argument and Colnett indignantly started to leave.

He stopped at the door when he heard: "Captain Colnett, you will make no move to sail to-day . . . nor will you sail at any future time."

Stunned, the latter whirled and asked angrily, "What do you mean, Captain Martinez?"

"You are not leaving here." The tone was heavy with insolence.

Captain Colnett's face grew red as he struggled to suppress his anger.

"What of your word, given to me only yesterday?"

"You will not question my orders." The Spaniard's dark eyes glittered. "If you are not careful . . . ."

Ignoring the warning Colnett said coldly,

"Our countries are not at war. You cannot hold me here; I will leave at my convenience."

"Captain Colnett, you will swing from the yardarm if you try to disobey me."

Martinez walked to the door and called out in Spanish.

An officer and three men hurried into the room. It was not long before Captain Colnett lay in the hold in chains, too anguished with regret to move. Why had he ignored that warning a man had risked his life to board his ship and give him? What of his responsibility to the men who had trusted him with this fur-trading enterprise? Thoughts such as these raced through his mind morning, noon and night during the days which followed. Finally, his mind broke under the strain. Insane, he was not aware of the fact his ship had been seized by Martinez and, like himself, his crew were prisoners. Alone and broken, Colnett lay in his dark dungeon in the hold of the *Princessa*.

The arrogant Don Martinez did not confine his cruelty to the white men. Chief Callicum was also his victim. Not understanding all that was going on at Friendly Cove, the chief was still trying to show friendship towards the Spaniards. A kindly, gentle man, he believed that as long as his people's rights were not interfered with he should not shun these strangers. But disturbing rumours had reached him about Captain Colnett, the man he admired. He had not had the opportunity to welcome his friend to his village. Innocently, he decided to take a gift of some exceptionally fine fish to Martinez and inquire about the Englishman.

Late one afternoon, his wife and child accompanying him, he set off in his canoe to visit the *Princessa*. He boarded the ship alone and asked to see Martinez. But when he offered his gift, instead of being treated with the courtesy he had expected, the Spaniard grabbed the fish from him in a rough manner and tossed them aside. He then arrogantly dismissed the chief. The Indian hid his hurt feelings but did not try to hide his disgust.

He stared into the cold, cruel eyes then muttered, "Peshae,

peshae!' meaning, "Bad, bad!" and then turned and started to the rail to climb down into his canoe. His words were understood and Martinez grabbed a rifle from one of his men standing beside him and fired at the native. He missed, but a soldier aimed and a bullet crashed into the unarmed and unsuspecting chief. His body fell into the water and disappeared before the horrified eyes of his wife and child who waited for him in the canoe.

His tribesmen standing on the shore saw this happen. A canoe shot from the beach and soon brought the widow and child back to the village. News of the murder spread. The natives were too stunned at first to think of revenge. Chief Callicum's old father hurried out to the *Princessa* and asked for permission to have divers hunt for his son's body. To the old man's outraged horror, Martinez refused this request. Sadly the father returned to shore and told of this further outrage. Then he realized how he could obtain this permission.

Knowing the greed of the Spaniard he returned with some priceless sea-otter skins and offered them in return for this grim favour. He got the permission. No Indian could allow a chief to lack a decent burial according to the ceremonies and customs of his people. But when the burial ceremonies were over, the Nootkans set out to avenge, in the only way they could, the murder of the chief they loved and respected. They refused to trade with Martinez and, shrewd as that man was, he did not realize what this meant until his trade-room was empty of furs.

Anxious to return to Mexico with his prisoners, he sailed for San Blas shortly after these events, proudly towing the plundered *Argonaut* with her helpless captain and crew aboard. His thoughts hurried ahead to the honours he felt sure would be heaped upon him when his superiors saw his prize.

But he was mistaken. His viceroy coldly reminded him of the orders he had received before he sailed from Mexico for Nootka. One of these orders had been to win the good-will of the Indians. Had he done that? Martinez thought of Chief Callicum's murder, then of the empty trade-room which had been the Indians' revenge. Another order had been to treat the commanders of English or other vessels with politeness and kindliness in view of existing peace between his country and theirs. The viceroy's tone was icy as he told the shaken Martinez of the stern note received that day from London. News of Captain Colnett's capture and the seizure of his ship had reached England. The result of Martinez' conduct at Nootka meant disaster for his country if something was not done to prevent it. England and Spain appeared to be on the brink of war over the possession of Nootka. Yet this man whose hot-tempered actions had done so much to bring this state of affairs about, sailed into port expecting to be rewarded for his actions.

The shaken offender winced as his superior stared coldly at him.

It was not a cruel, strutting Martinez who left his viceroy that day. It was a broken man, shorn of his command and sent away in disgrace.

Captive of an Indian Chief

The Story of John Jewett.

Maquinna, the famous Nootkan chief, plays a leading role in many of the dramas which marked the white man's earliest dealings with the Coast Indians. Scott never portrayed Highland hero more faithful to his friends, more jealous of his authority as chieftain, or more ruthless in his revenue for insult or injury, than this native warrior.

His long association with the Yorkshire-born John Jewett began with one of the bloodiest events of those days, the capture of the good ship *Boston* and the massacre of all but two of her crew.

John Jewett, son of a blacksmith of Hull, had eagerly devoured Captain Cook's accounts of his journeys, and had often listened spellbound, in his father's shop, to the stories of sea-captains whose ships were laid up for repairs. He longed to join in those voyages to newly discovered lands. At last he obtained a position as armourer on Captain Salter's ship *Boston* just before she sailed on her ill-fated expedition to Nootka. During the voyage he forged guns, knives, spear-heads and ornaments to trade for the Indians' furs.

The *Boston* reached Nootka Sound one day in March, 1803, and Captain Salter decided to drop anchor as he was in need of wood and fresh water. He wanted to make sure, however, before anyone went ashore, that the Indians were friendly who lived in the village confronting them. A number of canoes came out to the ship. Their occupants were allowed on board. First to reach the deck was the imposing figure of Maquinna, his eyebrows painted with two broad black stripes like new moons, and his long black hair, glistening with oil, bunched on top of his head. His hair was sprinkled with white eagle's down, the Indian symbol of peace. Thrown over his shoulders and reaching almost to the ground was a glistening robe of otter skins. His warriors wore cloaks of woven cedar bark.

Speaking in halting English, he welcomed Captain Salter and invited him to his village. The Captain thanked him and inquired about wood and fresh water. When the Chief offered to supply both, the Captain asked him and his men to stay for dinner on board and Maquinna eagerly accepted the invitation. He was then shown around the ship. His black eyes shone as he watched Jewett working at his forge below decks. He also showed special interest in the work of Thompson, the sailmaker, who was mending a torn sail. After a friendly meal, as the Indians were leaving, Captain Salter presented Maquinna with a fine gun Jewett had made. The Chief, delighted with this gift, asked the Captain to hunt with him next day and offered to send fresh salmon for the ship's larder.

However, the next morning Maquinna returned, one of his men carrying the gun he had been given. The locks on it were broken. The Chief explained that the gun had

broken when he tried to use it. The quick-tempered Captain
Salter was furious. He turned angrily to Jewett, who was
standing beside him, and asked if the gun could have been
defective. John assured him that it was one of the finest
he had ever made.

The Captain's temper flared. He called Maquinna a
liar. He accused him of deliberately breaking a fine gun
in order to get more presents in its place. Jewett looked
at Maquinna and saw that the Indian was greatly upset.
The blood rose under the copper skin as the native placed
a hand on his throat and then rubbed his breast. This
Jewett understood. It meant that Maquinna's heart had
risen to his throat in anger. Without a word the Chief
left the ship.

To the white men's surprise, the Indians returned the
next morning bringing gifts of salmon and game to trade
for knives and other articles. Maquinna appeared a short
time later and seemed to have forgotten the incident of
the day before. He was wearing a huge mask and carried
a handsomely carved rattle.

He said that he and his men wished to entertain Captain
Salter and his crew with songs and dances. Relieved by
this show of apparent friendliness on the part of the Indians,
Salter consented.

Maquinna began a weird rhythm with his rattles and
the performance started. Soon Jewett tired of the ceremonies and went below to his forge. He had not been
there long when he heard loud yells and heavy thuds from
the deck above. He rushed for the stairs and, just as he
reached the top, an arm appeared in the opening above
him and jerked him up by the hair. But the ribbon tying
it slipped through the Indian's hand and Jewett fell back

down the companionway, struck his head on the last step and was knocked unconscious.

When he came to, he looked up and saw that the hatch was closed. He heard the shouts of half-crazed Indians and realized with horror that they had taken the ship. Suddenly the hatch was lifted. An Indian appeared in this opening and motioned to Jewett to come up on deck.

Maquinna stood there surrounded by his warriors. Jewett shuddered as he saw the blood-stained deck, mute evidence of the fate of Captain Salter and his men. It appeared that all the others had been killed. Then Maquinna spoke, saying that Captain Salter's insults to him had been repaid. Jewett realized as the chief was talking that he understood more English than he had pretended, and had caught the meaning of Salter's hot words. Maquinna went on to say that John would not be killed if he consented to become the chief's slave and make weapons for him.

Jewett looked at the fierce, dark faces around him and realized that there was no way out. It was submission or death. Slowly he nodded. He was instantly seized and forced to kiss the chief's hands and feet in token of submission. Later he was ordered to run the ship into the cove.

When they reached the village, Jewett was happy to find that Thompson, the sail-maker, had also escaped the massacre. Maquinna had saved his life as well so that he could pursue his trade for him. With an armourer to make weapons and a sail-maker to make sails for his canoes, Maquinna would have a great advantage over enemy tribes.

The two white men settled into their strange life. When Thompson's hot temper sometimes brought threats of trouble, Jewett was able to calm him down; his tact in dealing with Maquinna was effective. But the two captives could see no hope of escape. On at least one occasion John was forced to accompany a war-party on a raid against another tribe; a raid which was successful largely due to the superiority of the weapons he had forged. Maquinna became fond of John Jewett and one day suggested that an Indian wife should be found for him. This, the chief explained, would appease his tribesmen who still wanted the two white men killed. They argued that if the white men were out of the way, they need not fear another white man's ship coming and finding out about the *Boston*. Jewett finally had to agree and an Indian bride was chosen. Maquinna had a lodge built for them and life became easier for the prisoners.

Then one day the chief from a neighboring village came to visit Maquinna. Jewett liked the man and felt he could trust him. He wrote a letter telling of his capture and asking for help. He slipped it to the visitor and begged him to deliver it to the first white man's ship he saw. The Indian was sympathetic and consented to do so.

However, time passed, and hope of rescue diminished. Then one morning, while John was busy at his forge, he heard a great commotion in the village. Amidst the confused noises, three cannon shots rang out and excited voices reached him, "White men . . . ships!" He ran to the beach where Thompson stood looking over the water, an expression of deep joy in his face. Jewett could hardly believe his eyes. A vessel was coming towards the shore. As they stood gazing at it with new-born hope, Maquinna came quietly up behind them. His voice was grave as he asked,

"You run away to ship, John?"

With an effort Jewett restrained his emotions. He realized that he must keep calm. Turning, he walked back to the forge where Maquinna soon joined him. The chief told John he had called a council of his warriors, for they must decide what was to be done about the two prisoners.

The two men waited anxiously for that decision for they knew that the Indians fully realized the danger of letting the white men live to tell the story of Captain Salter and his men. The Captain of the incoming ship would make them pay dearly for their crime. With the prisoners out of the way, they could blame another tribe for the massacre and thus cover their own guilt.

At last John and Thompson were called to Maquinna's lodge and learned that their lives would be spared on one condition. John must write a letter to the captain of the ship stating that they had stayed with Maquinna of their own free will and that they had been well treated. No mention must be made of Captain Salter or the rest of his crew. Maquinna would deliver the letter himself. John hastily agreed for he realized that, although Maquinna spoke English, he could not read it. Then he went to his lodge to write the letter.

When it was finished he called Thompson and showed it to him, and Thompson added his signature. Of course, the letter told the captain that Maquinna was responsible for the killing of Captain Salter and his men and that Thompson and he were captives. He asked that Maquinna be kept prisoner on board until Thompson and he managed to get to the ship. He handed the letter to Maquinna. The chief looked steadily into his eyes for a moment, and then said, "You no betray me, John?" John silently shook his head. This reply seemed to satisfy Maquinna and he called to his warriors, stepped into a canoe, and was swiftly carried out to the ship. With tense nerves the two white men waited on shore among the suspicious Indians.

Reaching the ship, Maquinna greeted the captain with a gift of rich furs. Then he presented the letter. The captain read it, looked at Maquinna, and called his men. Maquinna was soon in irons below decks.

In the meantime, John had managed to slip a gun to Thompson and arm himself. He now addressed the Indians. He wanted a canoe at once, he said, with two paddlers to take Thompson and himself out to the ship. He threatened that if the Indians refused, or tried to harm them, not only would Maquinna's head hang from the mast of the ship, but the ship's big guns would blow to pieces the village and all in it. For a moment the Indians hesitated, and then realizing the situation, they gave in.

Jewett reached the ship and gave its captain a full account of all that had occurred since the ill-fated *Boston* cast anchor at Nootka Sound. He then asked to see Maquinna who, he knew, still had in his possession the records of the *Boston*.

When Maquinna saw John he looked at him reproachfully and said, "I was your friend and you betrayed me, John!"

But John quickly removed the chains from Maquinna's hands and feet and told him he was getting off lightly for his crime. The chief was to go back to his village, return the records, and remember that he would always be treated fairly by the white men. In future, however, he would pay a heavy price for crimes committed against them.

With mixed feelings John watched Nootka Sound fade from sight the next morning. He could not shake off a sense of sadness at parting from its shores, nor could he forget Maquinna's last words.

No doubt in his way, the Nootkan Chief *had* tried to be his friend.

They Couldn't Say "No"

A Story of Alexander MacKenzie

The story of Alexander MacKenzie's memorable journey to find an overland route to the great Western Ocean is one of steadfast courage and stubborn persistence in the face of incredible hardships and difficulties. MacKenzie's indomitable will kept his little party moving steadily westward in spite of all the obstacles which mountain torrent and virgin forest could put in their way. From time to time during his long continuous struggle, incidents occurred which serve to bring out those qualities of bold leadership which marked the explorer. One such incident took place near what is now the town of Quesnel in the Cariboo.

The little party of explorers had come through Cottonwood Canyon which MacKenzie said, "was so violent we did not venture to run it." After successfully overcoming this hazard, the weary party journeyed doggedly on until rounding a bend in the river, they came upon signs of habitation.

Two small Indian canoes, empty, were gently swaying

with the movement of the water in front of them. A relieved cry burst from their lips. But this was cut short. An arrow sang by, narrowly missing the bow man of their own craft. They had hoped to find friendly natives and obtain canoes and food.

Instead, hostile Indians were hidden on the wooded shore nearby. Quick action was necessary.

MacKenzie at once ordered his Indian interpreter to call to their hidden assailants and tell them that they were friends. More arrows was the only reply. The bold explorer then told his men to pull towards the shore from which the arrows had come and, as they did so, he told them his plan in a few words.

He stood up in the canoe, unarmed, and stepped boldly ashore as soon as the canoe reached the bank. He carried a sack with him. While all eyes were centered on MacKenzie, the Indian interpreter, gun in hand, slipped unnoticed to the shelter of the woods.

Calmly, and with no trace of hesitation, the erect figure of the white man advanced towards the trees from which the arrows had come. His canoe shoved off and moved towards the opposite bank. Seemingly oblivious of the fact that dozens of pairs of dark eyes were watching his every move, MacKenzie halted and set down the sack. From it he pulled a mirror which flashed in the sunlight as he laid it on the ground. Next, he withdrew a string of gaudy beads which glittered as he placed them beside the looking-glass. One by one he took from the sack, and placed on the ground near the trees, a tempting array of ornaments. He turned his back to the glittering pile and, motionless, awaited the result.

The bushes parted and one brown face after another appeared. Then the first Indian stepped warily forward.

MacKenzie heard the soft footfalls of man after man but remained absolutely still. In a very few moments he could tell that the Indians had begun to finger the ornaments.

Then he turned and smiled at them as he motioned to the effect that he had brought them gifts. Instantly the strain was gone and soon a babble of excited voices filled the air.

One of them motioned to the white man to follow him and MacKenzie knew that the first step had been successfully taken in winning the friendship of these Indians. He obeyed the native's motioned invitation to recall his men and canoe to the shore. The relieved crew hastened to beach their craft and the Indian interpreter who had remained on call throughout the whole episode in case of danger to his leader, rejoined the party.

As they approached the nearby village, women and children ran out to meet them but pulled back in terror when they saw the white men. MacKenzie felt that he must win them over too. He halted and smilingy untied the almost empty sack he carried and looked around. One small boy was somewhat nearer than the rest, curiously and fearlessly gazing at the stranger. MacKenzie beckoned to him and held out his hand. The boy came slowly forward, his large black eyes staring into the friendly blue ones of the white man. The other children gasped in astonishment as the boy reached out a grubby hand and took what MacKenzie held out to him.

Looking about him, he saw the envious, admiring glances of his young friends and then, following the motions of the white man, he opened his hand and popped what it held into his mouth. There was a tense silence as children and grown-ups watched his face intently.

A smile spread over his face, his eyes glistened with

pleasure, and he smacked his lips noisily. It was indeed a tasty morsel that this stranger had given him.

A moment later and MacKenzie was surrounded by boys and girls begging for their share. Laughing heartily, he started handing out pieces to them and called out happily to his men, "Our maple sugar seems to be very popular."

The Snow Bird

The Story of Lady Douglas

The story of Nellie Douglas, First Lady of British Columbia, begins at Fort Churchill. She was the youngest daughter of William Connolly, the chief factor of that important trading post on Hudson Bay. Shy and sensitive, the Snowbird, as Nellie was often called because of her fair skin, blonde hair, and blue eyes, was a favourite with Indian and whiteman alike.

Her father was immensely proud of the great company he served, and did everything possible to impress both his subordinates and the Indians of the region with its power and importance, and with the dignity of his own position as its representative. To Nellie herself, the name, "Governor and Company of Adventurers of England Trading into Hudson's Bay", was none too high sounding a title for that great institution, the Hudson's Bay Company, with which her whole life was bound up.

Close to her childhood home were the ruins of old Fort Prince of Wales. Nellie was fascinated by the stories her father told about that once famous stronghold. She loved to climb the crumbling stone wall, now covered with vines, and picture the scenes of the past. In her imagination men in scarlet coats with brass buttons rode through the gates of the fort; French Canadian voyageurs, gay in their coloured sashes and bright caps, stepped singing from the canoes of the arriving fur-brigades; and Indians, wearing blankets or beaded buckskin jackets, came to exchange their valuable furs for the attractive trade goods piled high on the company's shelves. But she refused to think of that day when three French vessels of war sailed into Hudson's Bay and took possession of the old fort in the name of the French king. She was proud to think that her own Fort Churchill had taken the place of Fort Prince of Wales and that some of the gay scenes she loved to picture to herself were repeated there.

Mr. Connolly was moved from one northern outpost to another while Nellie was growing up, and she and her family came to know most of that western wilderness. When she was still young and her father was in charge of Cumberland House in Northern Saskatchewan, the famous explorer Sir James Franklin visited them. He and his party were on their last, ill-fated expedition to the Arctic. They spent the winter at the trading-post and while the Indians and company employees made sleighs and snow-shoes, and the native women sewed moccasins and parkas, the visitors were entertained by the chief factor and his family. These last days of preparation passed pleasanty and quickly for everyone.

There was an artist in the party who was recording on canvas the important features of the expedition. He grew fond of the Connolly children and, delighted with Nellie's delicate colouring, painted her portrait. Later, after Franklin and his party were lost, Lady Franklin came to search for her husband. She met Nellie and told how the portrait had been sent to her in England with some of the artist's historical paintings. Of them all, she said, she had been particularly impressed by the picture of the shy, sensitive girl. There was a measure of comfort for the widow in meeting the family with whom her husband had spent his last happy days.

Mr. Connolly was finally moved to Fort St. James, then the most important fort in western New Caledonia. The fur-traders of the Babine country and north from Fraser Forks to the Russian boundary brought their furs to Fort St. James. When they arrived with their fur-laden craft, everyone at the fort was down by the water to greet them.

One day a tall, young Scotsman stepped out of one of the boats. James Douglas had been sent to Fort St. James as Mr. Connolly's assistant. Douglas soon settled into the work at the trading post, and Mr. Connolly realized that the young Scot was a hard worker with a real capacity for leadership.

Nellie was only sixteen years old when she fell in love with James Douglas. In spite of her youth, her father consented to her marriage and the wedding was celebrated in fine style. The long table in the mess hall was loaded with pewter and silver dishes filled with food which testified to the skill of the French Canadian chef. Toasts and compliments were showered on the pretty bride and her groom. Dinner was followed by music and dancing which lasted throughout the night.

The following year, Nellie's wisdom and courage were put to a severe test. Her father, accompanied by most of the men from the fort, had gone on an inspection trip and young Douglas was left in charge. He had only one or two men and Nellie's small brothers to help with the work.

One morning, while they were at breakfast, they heard loud, angry voices in the courtyard. The interpreter came running in to say that armed Indians demanded to see Douglas. They claimed the white men were responsible for the death of one of their tribe. Douglas instructed the interpreter to go out and tell them to leave their guns on the ground and go into the trade room where he would talk to them.

When he faced the Indians a short time later Douglas saw they were in an ugly mood. His wife slipped into the room and stood unnoticed, listening to their demands and to her husband's replies as he reasoned with the Chief. He urged him to wait until Mr. Connolly returned, when grievances would be dealt with fairly. Still unnoticed by the angry natives, Nellie beckoned to her brothers, quietly left the room, and stood for a moment whispering to them. Then she returned and joined her husband. For some unknown reason her appearance enraged the Indians. One of them sprang forward and seized her, another rushed up with knife in hand. He raised his arm as the Indian holding her drew back her head and bared her throat.

At that moment her older brother ran into the room and saw what was happening. Using a flying tackle, he grabbed the Indian around the knees, forcing him to release Nellie. The native sprawled to the floor, knocking his accomplice off balance so that the knife fell from his hand.

In the meantime the tall, powerfully built Douglas was holding his own and managing to edge his way to where a gun stood by the door. His few assistants were effectively wielding chairs and any other weapons that came to hand.

Then the Indian who had been knocked down got up and hurried outside. He was back in a moment with his gun. Aiming at Douglas, he pulled the trigger. There was no report. The gun was empty. He shouted to the others to hurry outside and get their muskets. Soon they all stood with empty guns in their hands. The room suddenly grew quiet as the natives looked at one another in superstitious fear. Douglas took advantage of this moment to seize the gun he had been trying to reach. The chief called to his bewildered men and there was an excited roar of voices. Then Douglas was heard shouting above the tumult and the other voices sank into silence as he spoke to them. He told them that a fate worse than mysteriously emptied guns would overtake them if they did not leave the fort at once. Intimidated as much by the young Scotsman's stern expression as by the weapon in his hands, they turned and left the room. The last Indian had barely disappeared before the palisade gates were locked. Douglas ordered them kept that way until Mr. Connolly returned.

The young husband was rightfully proud of his wife's courage and quick thinking. But Nellie insisted modestly that her brothers had been the brave ones. It had been her suggestion, it was true, that they slip outside and empty the Indians' guns, but they were the ones who had done so and it had been their own idea to pour water into them.

Not long after this, Sir George Simpson ordered young Douglas's transfer to Fort Vancouver where he would serve under Dr. John McLoughlin, Chief Factor of Oregon. His wife, however, was unable to accompany him but stayed with her family until her first baby was born a short time after. The baby died soon after birth, and then, as soon as she was strong enough, Mrs. Douglas set off to join her husband. Her father accompanied her on the hazardous trip with one of the boat brigades.

Nellie Douglas's home in Fort Vancouver was comfortable and she was very happy there. There was more excitement

and more social life than at any other fort where she had
lived. Dr. McLoughlin, an imposing figure of a man six
feet six inches tall, with a partriarchal white beard and long
hair, followed the custom of manor life in England. His
home overlooking the Columbia River was a centre of
lavish hospitality. At dinner not only were good food and
wines served, but witty conversation added to the guests'
enjoyment. Dr. McLoughlin always insisted that every person at table contribute something to the conversation or
read an excerpt from some book which would lead to
general discussion. Nellie Douglas revelled in and learned
much from these table conversations. She became thoroughly
acquainted with the social duties which devolved upon the
first lady of a large garrison.

The climate of Fort Vancouver was too damp for her,
however, and she welcomed her husband's transfer to Fort
Victoria on Vancouver Island. Here they made their permanent home and brought up their family of six daughters
and one son. Here, as wife of the Governor of Vancouver
Island, Nellie Douglas became the gracious chatelaine of
the fort where the city of Victoria now stands.

On one memorable occasion she and her husband were
entertaining at dinner. Sir Matthew Begbie, recently
knighted and made Chief Justice of British Columbia, sat
on her right. The servants had brought in liqueurs, and
Nellie Douglas was sitting quietly for a few minutes admiring the play of candle light on the cut glass. Her attention
was brought back to her guests when Sir Mathew stood
up, went to her husband's side, and quietly placed a crimson
collar and pendant around his host's neck. Next he fastened
a star-shaped, jewelled pin on his coat.

James Douglas had just received the order of Knight
Commander of the Bath! Reaching for his glass, *Sir James*

Douglas stood straight and proud as he gave the toast "To the Queen". Nellie looked up at her tall, dignified husband, her pride in his success too deep for more than a shy smile. This quiet, intimate ceremony always remained one of her dearest memories.

A moment later she was made to realize for the first time her share in her husband's honours. When the Chief Justice proposed the next toast, it was "To Lady Douglas, wife of the Governor and First Lady of British Columbia."

Miner's Law Ends on the Fraser

The Story of Ned McGowan's War

Ned McGowan caused more excitement and trouble than any other bold rascal who swaggered into the mining camps during the gold rush in British Columbia. He led an uprising of miners along the Fraser River which brought the Royal Engineers and the navy rushing to the scene. In fact, the Royal Engineers had barely arrived in our province when they were off to Hill's Bar to put an end to Ned McGowan's war.

The Fraser River gold rush was at its height and mining camps were springing up overnight. Hill's Bar was one of these and its rich diggings had attracted miners from the United States as well as from other parts of Canada.

A mile or two up the river stood Yale which had been founded by the Hudson's Bay Company as a fur-trading post some years before the gold rush. It considered itself the logical centre of all activities. It was not only a mining camp in its own right, but also, standing at the head of navigation on the Fraser River, a supply depot for the camps

farther up the river and in the Cariboo. There was great
rivalry between Yale and Hill's Bar.

When Ned McGowan arrived from the United States he
chose Hill's Bar as his centre of operations. He reached
the new mining camp with a number of doubtful companions. Strange rumours drifted across the border in their
wake. One of these was that Ned had been a judge in
California but had been thrown off the bench for crooked
practice.

He and his gang soon made their presence felt so that no
owner of a promising claim was safe from them. If Ned's
glib tongue could not trick the miner out of his claim,
the gang moved in and took it by force. But, as yet, a
plausible story had eased McGowan around every dangerous
corner. The people in Hill's Bar were divided in their
opinion of him. To his admirers, won over by his charming
manners, ready smile and free spending, he remained a
good fellow; but he was branded by his victims, rapidly
growing in number, as a scoundrel.

Law enforcement was to a great extent in the hands of
the miners themselves. Magistrates had been appointed in
some centres, Hill's Bar and Yale for example, but their
attempts to maintain order were subject to the whims of
the miners.

It was during a holiday celebration that matters reached
a climax for Ned McGowan. He and his companions had
gone to Yale to celebrate in their usual rowdy manner.
Miners, prospectors and pack-train operators thronged the
dance halls, gambling houses and saloons. Nuggets and gold
dust flowed as freely as liquor. One of the celebrants from
Hill's Bar got into a fight with a negro. He beat his victim
mercilessly and left him lying unconscious on the floor of
the saloon. He continued to celebrate until his poke was

empty then, returning to Hill's Bar with his companions, he forgot about the fight. It was brought sharply back to his mind when, a few days later, the local magistrate received a warrant for his arrest from the magistrate at Yale.

When Ned McGowan heard of the warrant he was loudly indignant at what he termed legal impudence on the part of the Yale magistrate. He drew large crowds about him as he denounced this action. His fine-sounding phrases roused his listeners to fever pitch. Even the local magistrate was impressed and indignant. Excited knots of men gathered in the saloons protesting against what was called "Interference by that magistrate at Yale!" McGowan soon had the jealousy of the rival town fanned into flame. Meantime, the victim of the warrant was surprised and embarrassed by the sympathy he received from men who assured him that no one was going to interfere with a hard-working miner's right to celebrate; nor should a bar-room fight be taken seriously. Ned patted the bewildered man on the back and assured him everything would be all right. He had an idea . . . their magistrate must issue a warrant for the arrest of the negro. This was done and Ned and his crowd cheered the messenger who rode off to Yale with the warrant.

But when the messenger delivered it he was promptly arrested and thrown into jail. Feeling now rose dangerously high in both camps. Miners deserted their diggings and stormed the rival towns to voice their opinions. Camp was pitched against camp and, while so far words were the only weapons used, threats of more serious action filled the air.

As is so often the case where mob violence threatens, an unscrupulous leader seized the opportunity to exercise his power. Ned McGowan now came into his own as a leader.

A meeting of all the miners around Hill's Bar was called and Ned's oratory was at its best as he harangued the crowd. The result was a decision to form a posse and march on Yale to deal with its presumptuous magistrate.

McGowan, a tall, bold figure, led the men who slipped through the darkness into Yale that night. He was the first to step over the magistrate's threshold. Before that startled man could gather his sleepy wits together, Ned and his followers had hustled him off to the river. The poor man was forced into a boat by the grim, silent men who surrounded him and, off he went to Hill's Bar. Ned presided over the miner's court which forced the outraged magistrate to pay a fine. With a solemn warning against ever again interfering with celebrating visitors, he was set free.

When he returned to Yale and told his friends what had happened, the town seethed with indignation. But indignation soon turned to apprehension and apprehension to fear. If this incident went unnoticed and the marauders from Hill's Bar went unpunished, what would happen next? The question was on the lips of every citizen of Yale. Word was rushed to Governor Douglas in Victoria that the miners were in revolt. The people of Yale begged him to help them and take immediate steps to restore order.

Luckily, when this news reached him, Governor Douglas was in a position to act at once, owing to a number of recent events. A detachment of Royal Engineers under Colonel Moody had been sent from England and had just arrived. Also, Matthew Baillie Begbie had been sworn in as "Judge in the Colony of British Columbia." The Governor decided to discuss the miner's uprising under Ned McGowan's leadership with Judge Begbie before giving Colonel Moody his orders.

Matthew Begbie smiled to himself as he listened, remembering his final interview in England with the colonial secretary, Mr. Bulwer-Lytton. The latter had told him that his duties in the new land would be "unusual". After hearing this account of the insurgent miners and their leader, Begbie understood now what that meant. He stroked his well-trimmed beard and his eyes twinkled as he thought of this bold man who had placed the magistrate at Yale in so undignified a position. Begbie was here to establish crown law and though it might be difficult, it appeared that it would not be a monotonous task. He returned his attention to what Governor Douglas was now saying.

"I might not take this affair so seriously were it not for what happened in Oregon when John McLoughlin was in charge of Fort Vancouver."

"That was the time of the cry, 'Fifty-four—forty, or fight,' which ended in our losing Oregon to the Americans, was it not?" asked the Judge.

'Yes," replied Douglas. "The American settlers flooded into the Hudson's Bay domain down there. Vigilante committees were set up by men much like this Ned McGowan. These same committees became rallying points when England's claim to those lands was challenged."

"Perhaps this is merely a case of miner's law in the hands of a reckless man," suggested Begbie.

"I do not think so. However, I shall send Colonel Moody and his detachment as well as Captain Mayne with his blue-jackets. Such a show of force will teach these people that they are not so isolated as they think and that transportation is quicker than they had realized. I should like you to accompany Captain Mayne on his ship." The Governor rang a bell adding, "We must take no chance of losing our gold fields here as we did our fur trade in Oregon."

Judge Begbie nodded and stood up. "If there is nothing more you wish to say about this matter I shall attend to some correspondence before preparing for the journey."

"I need not say that I am confident you will deal with McGowan in a wise manner," said the Governor dryly then, turning as a servant entered, he ordered, "Present my compliments to Colonel Moody and Captain Mayne and ask them to come here at once."

It was a truly formidable expedition that set out from Victoria for Hill's Bar. Colonel Moody and his Royal Engineers arrived there first and found McGowan and his companions still flushed with victory, and boasting that they would enforce any law required on that part of the river. Moody first met McGowan as he walked up the main street. They recognized each other at first glance. The Colonel had barely begun to speak before McGowan, cold eyes boring into his, drawled insolently, "If you don't want any trouble, you'd better take your men and clear out. We don't want you around here"

Colonel Moody controlled himself, realizing that he must wait for the arrival of Judge Begbie and Captain Mayne before taking action. He had not long to wait. Governor Douglas would no doubt have been satisfied had he seen the surprised faces of Ned and his insurgents. When confronted with this formidable array of uniforms and arms, Ned decided instantly that his brief rule of Hill's Bar was over and he disappeared from the camp.

That night soldiers and sailors patrolled the wooden sidewalks and the small town was strangely quiet. The saloons and dancehalls no longer echoed with loud music and

rowdy songs; instead, the miners slipped quietly back to
their cabins.

Into this nervous, uneasy quiet came word that Judge
Begbie had ordered the arrest of Ned McGowan. Everyone
left in the town waited for their "bad man" to defy the
newly arrived representatives of law and order. Now was
his chance to make good his boast of running Hill's Bar
to suit himself, his companions and friends. But Ned again
surprised everyone.

A tall stranger walked quietly into Begbie's cabin. With
a disarming smile he held out his hand and welcomed the
Judge to Hill's Bar. Casually, he announced that he was
Ned McGowan and invited the Judge and his entire party
to a banquet he was giving in their honour. Repressing a
smile at the man's impudence, Judge Begbie politely
accepted the invitation.

Word soon got about among the miners that Ned
McGowan's war was over and the "bad man" had been
subdued. The miners relaxed and turned their attention
to the anticipated banquet.

That celebration was one of the best the mining camp
had known and food and champagne was dispensed liberally
to everyone. Ned McGowan regained any prestige he might
have lost with the miners . . . until later when they found
that they had to foot the bills for the night's lavish hospitality.

But the morning was a new day and the Judge's turn.
The wily Ned got a jolt when Begbie hailed him into court,
set up in his cabin. There was no twinkle in the Judge's eye
as he fined him the amount Ned had fined Yale's magistrate.
He warned him sternly against further misdeeds. When
Judge Begbie finished speaking, it was a very subdued
McGowan who paid the fine and offered his apologies.

Before he left Hill's Bar Matthew Begbie called the miners together and told them that the laws of England were to be enforced on the mainland of British Columbia. He warned them against taking that law into their own hands in the future. The room was silent when he finished speaking and the miners glanced uneasily at one another. They realized that something very important to each one of them had happened in that small room. Not only was Ned McGowan's war finished; miner's law on the river had also come to an end.

Blood Stains on the Snow

The Legend of the Forbidden Plateau.

When the pioneers came to the Comox Valley they found a land of plenty. There was good fishing and hunting, and rich soil for farming, so they were not surprised to learn that the Indians called it, "Komox", meaning, "Land of Plenty".

These pioneers came from Australia, the British Isles and Eastern Canada, lured to British Columbia by tales of gold in the Cariboo. When they had failed to make their fortunes in the creeks of the mainland, they had decided to farm in the lovely Comox Valley on Vancouver Island. In time more settlers had arrived.

Mrs. James Robb came to Comox in 1862 with her husband and three children. There was no white woman there to greet her and she had to spend the first day or so in an Indian woman's home in the native village. Her husband soon built a temporary shelter for his family and they moved into it until their permanent home was built.

The day this home was finished Mrs. Robb looked about her and sighed with contentment and pride. The small house was built of stout logs and had two bedrooms upstairs and three rooms downstairs. The children were given the two upper bedrooms and their mother soon arranged every detail for their comfort. The feather beds she had brought with other possessions from England added a homey note to the neat little rooms. Downstairs, her flower-sprigged china was arranged to advantage on shelves above a chest of drawers. Two brass candlesticks shone on the long wooden dining-table which had benches on either side. In the kitchen stood Mrs. Robb's most prized possession, her stove, which she had brought with her at great inconvenience and expense but with equal determination. Pewter pots hung from wooden pegs. It was a cozy, cheerful room with the glowing stove throwing out its warmth. No householder could be prouder than this pioneer woman was as she looked about her small rooms when everything was in place.

Her husband, who had made most of the furniture, shared her pride. He had built their home close to the water and the forest crept almost to their door. Sunshine and dew fell on delicate fern and sturdy bracken and distilled a fragrance which mingled with that of the wild flowers. The high, sweet song of birds in nearby woods brought memories of her home in England. The first night in her new home, Mrs. Robb was awakened by the howling of wolves in the forest and she was terrified. But she thought of the stoutly barred door and her husband's gun, and felt relieved. She forced herself to think of the many things she had to do when day came and finally went back to sleep.

There was little time for this courageous woman to feel lonely or homesick. As the months passed the farm became a reality and began to repay the Robbs for their hard work. On a slope above the beach stood the barn. A root house held vegetables which had been gathered and stored there for winter use. They bought a team of oxen and a cow and more land was ploughed. Mrs. Robb's home-made bread, cakes and pies became very popular with the lonely bachelors who shared them. The son of the family was, in time, old enough to help his father and more stock was bought. The girls were able also to do their share of the work and helped their mother with household chores. The farm prospered and grew.

Evenings were a pleasant time in that pioneer home. The tinkle of cow-bells mingled with the sleepy song of the birds. Father and son returned from cutting hay or ploughing in stump-dotted fields, fenced in by fire-blackened logs. In the little log home supper waited for the two weary farmers. As soon as they arrived the long table was heaped with tempting food and the family started their evening meal. There was no surprise shown when a knock on the door announced an uninvited guest who was welcomed heartily.

Mrs. Robb mothered the lonely settlers who came to her home for companionship. All enjoyed the merry atmosphere she created in it. She saw many of them through a bout of home-sickness and nursed them when they were ill. Men-of-war arrived at Comox bringing more settlers and both sailors and passengers shared the Robbs' lavish hospitality.

The Indians also came from their village and this kindly woman did what she could to help them. She nursed many a sick native woman and child. They were awed at first by her home. The glowing stove held their attention until they saw the brass candle-sticks. One young man could not resist their shining temptation and tried to steal them. But Mrs. Robb soon made him see his mistake. She picked up a huge stick and chased him until he dropped them. She was not bothered by that young man again.

One day Mrs. Robb and her young daughters went to the beach to dig clams. Mary, an old Indian woman, joined them. As Mrs. Robb was talking to her she looked across the water and stopped speaking. Mary's black eyes followed her gaze, then in a frightened voice the old woman quavered, "Haidas! War-canoe!" The two women stared at the huge canoe which was approaching. It was close enough for them to see the spur-shaped stern and jutting prow which were carved with odd figures. These looked like the head and long tapering neck and shoulders of some mythical sea-creature. But the white woman forgot the canoe when she saw what was in it. Indians, their faces painted in weird designs, some wearing hideous masks, were chanting, their voices rising in volume as they drew nearer. Turning, she saw the terror on her children's faces and realized she must do something. Mary's wrinkled brown face was twisted with fear as she spoke.

"They come from village they raid, kill many men, now they go back home. Song they sing tells of fight they win." The old woman trembled as her eyes darted towards the forest. Her brown hand reached out and she grabbed the little girl next to her and started to run. "Quick, we go into woods, wait till they go, not let them see us."

They ran and soon reached the shelter of the trees. The little group huddled together, silent. Mrs. Robb regained her control and tried to keep her voice calm as she turned to Mary and said,

"Well, we are safe here. Now, we must forget what we saw and remember they will soon be gone. Mary, will you tell us a story? I have always wanted to hear about the Forbidden Plateau; will you tell us about it?"

Mary nodded gravely, then began her story.

"Maybe you wonder why snow on mountain turns colour of blood when summer moons come. I tell you why this is. My people believe that before they came here, white, hairy giants lived on those mountains. But we never see them. So our young people laugh and say they not there, just old women believe in them. But old people shake their heads and warn them to look out. Comox people have good life in those days. Big cedar trees grow all round so our men cut them down, split logs and make our lodges, strong and warm. Hunters bring back plenty meat and skins of wild animals for our women to make clothes. We dry meat and dig roots, pick wild berries on hills. Plenty fish in waters. We eat, dance and sing our songs and have great happiness. No one think of enemies or war. But both come. Scouts spy on us and we not know they are there. They watch our hunters come with rich furs and meat, fishermen with lots of fish. They go back and tell their people this. They tell people, too, that we are not ready for war, we not fight.

But they not know of Hamatsa. Our men who belong to Hamatsa, what you call Secret Society, they go to woods when they reach maybe fourteen, fifteen years, they live alone there for many days. They live in special lodge deep in forest, alone, no food, fire or weapons. They must grow strong, never be afraid, and find Good Spirit, or helper who will look after them and protect them. When they come back to us they are strong, brave and belong to Hamatsa.

They are our warriors. They know of danger from enemy and warn us. Maybe they see scouts in forest who spy on us. They make our old, wise men believe them and get ready for attack. Council is called and all agree to send women and children to mountain to be safe from enemy when they come.

So when time comes warriors take women and children to Plateau. But old men think again of hairy white giants and feel afraid. They say perhaps this is not what we should do. Some of them say our women and children may be harmed by these Evil Ones. They be safer with our men. They tell how these giants get mad sometime and come out of caves in rocks. They not like people to be there. They throw these people from edge of canyon down to rocks below. Maybe they do this to our people.

But warriors say these stories not true. They say enemy will kill our women and children or take them slaves if they win fight; up there in mountain they not find them. Warriors, too, tell men they must hurry and be ready, attack come soon. So women and children go.

"Enemy come and all too busy fighting to think of other things. Our men fight long and hard and in end they win. They kill many and drive others away. Next day they sing war songs, winning songs, as they climb mountain to bring women and children home.

"But when they get to Plateau they stop singing. They see no one so they call, loud, long, but no answer. Not one woman or child there to speak to them. Then they see blood on snow. No sound, only wind it moans in trees. They hunt until too tired to walk more. They come back and look at blood on snow. They moan like wind in trees, even warriors. Then a sound comes to them and it is like evil laughter. An old man trembles and tells them it is hairy white giants who laugh at them. They all remember stories about what these giants do to people when they get mad. They have killed our women and children. Our men turn and go down to village. No one speaks.

That night our Chief speaks and he says plateau is forbidden and Comox people will never go there. Many moons pass and one old man lives who tell this story. It come to us from father to son and to grandson. Each year, same time, snow turns red like blood, blood of women and children who died there, killed by Evil Ones. Now, some of our young people say this is old man's tale and not true but we do not go to Forbidden Plateau."

The old Indian woman stopped speaking and her black eyes were filled with shadows from the past. The children stirred restlessly and their mother jumped up, saying,

"It was just the story to turn our fears from the present danger. We all forgot it while you were talking, Mary. Wait here and I'll see if the canoe has gone."

She was back in a short time and said cheerfully, "They've gone, we can go home now. Come along, Mary, and have something to eat with us. Thank you for telling us your story. Now I understand what your people mean when they speak of the Forbidden Plateau."

That evening when the children were in bed, Mrs. Robb told her husband Mary's story. He nodded as he said,

"It may be superstitious nonsense as some of our neighbours call it, but these Indians, living close to nature as they do, have a reason which is local to them for these strange facts. It is true, the snow on the Plateau does turn red each year."

FOOTNOTE: The scientific explanation for the snow turning red is the presence of a very small, reddish organism, termed Algae Sphaerella, which exists in the snow in great quantities.

On the Warpath

The Story of the Chilcotin Massacres.

The Chilcotin country, the great plain-land between the coast and the Cariboo, was a rich country, and the Chilcotin Indians a proud people. Horses were their prize possessions and they learned to ride almost as soon as they learned to walk. They were good hunters and their camps were plentifully supplied with game and fish. They lived a satisfying life following the customs of their forefathers, and in their isolation, knew little and cared less about the white man's laws.

But furs and gold put an end to this isolation as white men appeared to establish ranches, open trading posts or operate pack-trains into the Cariboo. The fur-traders encouraged the native hunters to bring their furs to the trading posts and in return provided them with blankets, guns, ammunition and foods they had never known before. The Indian way of life was modified in many ways, and the Chilcotin chiefs began to resent these changes which tended to destroy their old authority over their people. The white men recognized only their own law and their ideas of justice were very different from those of the Indians.

One change which caused bitterness was brought about when construction started on a new road which was to run through the Chicotin country and open it up to the white man for all time. This was known as Waddington's Bute Inlet-Fraser River Road. The new road would run from the head of Bute Inlet up the Homanthko River and water-ways leading to Tatla Lake to join the Bentinck Arm-Fraser River trail which had been opened in 1862. It would provide a shorter route from the coast to the Cariboo and serve many of the miners better than the Governor Douglas Road, as the Cariboo Road was often called.

Mr. Waddington, a far-seeing, energetic man, was responsible for the new road. He felt the building of this road would mean a more thorough development of the riches of the Cariboo. Also, supplies brought over this shorter route would be less epensive to the miners.

Construction of the new road got under way and a hardy crew of construction workers was recruited. Equipment and supplies were shipped to the head of Bute Inlet. The formidable task of cutting a road through the wilderness was started.

William Brewster, the foreman, was a capable, practical organizer and did all in his power to minimize the hardships and discomforts for his men. The men, in turn, respected Brewster and progress was rapid. The construction party at first found the Indians friendly and co-operative and went unarmed.

But the Chilcotin chiefs were not interested in Waddington's reasons for building a road through their country. They only saw in this a further threat to their way of life and the eventual loss of their hunting grounds.

Klattassin, one of their principal chiefs, decided to put an end to some of the wrongs, real or fancied, for which he held the whites responsible. A powerful speaker in council, he harangued his own followers and other chiefs. He succeeded in persuading a goodly number to join him in an attempt to drive out the intruders and return to their ancient way of life.

It was a mild evening that April in 1864, and the men of the construction gang were sitting in front of the cook tent enjoying their evening smoke when the first hints of Indian trouble were voiced among them.

"You know, boys, I was told we might have trouble with these Chilcotins," said Brewster, knocking the ashes from his pipe, "but that simply shows how little the people in Victoria know about them."

Charles Buttles frowned as he glanced at his chief. "I've been a bit worried about something which happened today," he said, "Perhaps I should have told you about this sooner. You know Chief Klattassin? He came around this morning with some of his braves. They rode up to where my gang was working, and without asking leave, drew our Indians into a parley. I didn't understand what they said but I didn't like it. His manner was cocky. After he had gone our Indian workers muttered among themselves and looked sullen when I told them to get back to work."

"You should have told me about this before, Charlie." Brewster's voice was edged with annoyance.

"I didn't think it amounted to much but now its got me wondering. That's why I brought it up."

The man sitting next to him spoke up, "And another funny thing, I ran across some of Klattassin's men this afternoon back on the trail. They ducked into the bushes when I came along but I could have sworn their faces were painted. Looked mighty like they had their war-paint on."

William Brewster's face was serious as he listened to this. He stood up and paced back and forth for a moment. "There may be nothing to all this but we can't afford to take any chances. We'll put a guard on the store house and the ferry. Tim, you go on guard there; the ammunition may be what they have in mind. Klattassin may think he needs that or some food. That's probably what they're after."

Tim Smith laughed, "Trust an Indian to think of his belly. But they won't get anything tonight if they come looking for it."

Later that night, Tim sat on a log idly watching the moon-rippled water as it gently washed the shore. He heard a slight rustling behind him, but seeing nothing when he went to investigate, he decided that some small animal was responsible for the noise. As dawn began to spread its glow over the sky he grew sleepy and stretched out against a log.

He did not see the dark eyes watching him, nor did he see the shadowy forms as they sprang upon him.

The rest of the road-crew were asleep in their tents, unaware of the silent figures now creeping towards them. The first knife slashed at their tents and the pegs were torn loose before they were fully awake. Too late, they tried desperately to save themselves. It was all over in a very few minutes and ten men were dead.

Klattassin and his followers made their next lightning attack on a party of packers and miners. This party had been travelling along the Bentinck Arm trail towards the Fraser, carrying supplies to the men working on Waddington's road.

Alexander MacDonald, the owner of the pack train, had

lived for many years in that country. His pack train had made more money for him than most of the prospectors had taken from their claims. He had not noticed any active unrest on the part of the Indians and so far this trip had gone as quietly as usual. He rode along confidently, keeping a casual eye on his horses. He smiled to himself as he watched an awkward colt try to rub its pack off on a tree as it passed.

His attention was suddenly diverted and he jerked his horse to a halt as he saw a party of Indians coming towards him. As they approached he was surprised to see them spread out in such manner as to make it impossible to pass. As the first two reached him riding abreast, he called to them to drop into single file, adding angrily that the trail was too narrow for such risks in passing. The Indians stared insolently at him, but as the pack train moved steadily forward they called back to their companions and then obeyed the white man's orders. One of the packers rode up to MacDonald and the two men remarked on the unusual and disturbing incident as the Indians disappeared around a curve in the trail.

"Looked ugly, didn't they? Almost seemed as though they wanted to tumble freight and horses off the trail."

"Yes," answered MacDonald, "the whole thing was queer. I don't like it, but it may not be anything to worry about; just a few fool Indian bucks with a chip on their shoulder." He dismissed the matter from his mind.

The rest of the day passed without further incident and that evening they made camp close to a stretch of green pasture where the horses could graze. Around the fire, after the evening meal, talk turned to the usual topics of the latest rich strike made by some lucky prospector, incidents of the trail, and the staggering prices the miners had to pay for supplies.

"Waddington may be foolish according to those people down in Victoria," said one of the miners in the party, "but his new road is sure going to make a lot of difference to us in my part of the Cariboo."

"Make it easier for us all," MacDonald replied. "The only ones who don't like the road are the Indians. I hear that hot-headed chief of theirs, Klattassin, is doing a lot of talking about it."

One of the packers spoke up, "These Chilcotin Indians are good at talking and grumbling about things but they're a lot better off now that Brewster, the construction boss, gives them work with good wages."

"Sure they are, and they know it," another added. "It's only a few trouble-makers that object to our coming here."

The men turned in early, knowing that dawn would see them on the trail again. They were too tired to stay awake long and the whole camp was soon wrapped in silence.

Dawn's light had barely swept away the darkness when the pack train started on its way. The still, fresh air of the morning laid a silence on the men as they rode into the growing warmth of the sun-splashed trail.

Suddenly the silence was shattered and a shrieking, maddened band of horsemen dashed from the bushes and were upon them. The Indians, decked out in full war paint and led by Chief Klattassin, scored a complete surprise.

MacDonald fell wounded at the first onslaught and a slashing knife ended his struggles. The completeness of the surprise, however, served many of the white men well, for the crazed pack horses dashed off in panic and, with packs dragging, wildly tried to escape through the oncoming Chilcotins. In the ensuing bedlam, before the attackers could disengage themselves from the burdened animals, those members of their victim's party who had not been shot down in the first moment of the attack were able to reach the shetler of the forest.

The next victim to feel the Indians' vengeance was Alexander McLean, a settler who had served with the Hudson's Bay Company. When he heard of the massacres he promptly decided to contact a group of Indians he had known for years. He felt sure that through them something might be done to end the trouble. McLean slipped away alone to carry out his mission.

He never knew when he was first spotted by the insurgents. He was shot down without seeing his killers.

By now every white settler in the Chilcotin lived in terror, not knowing who the next victim would be. It was a rancher living alone on Benshee Lake. He was surprised and murdered inside his log cabin.

The Chilcotin massacres were beginning to assume the appearance of all-out war against the white man and almost unbearable tension was setting in amongst even the most courageous.

Owing to the isolation and difficulties of travel, it was some time before Governor Seymour in Victoria heard what was happening in the Chilcotin country. When news reached him he acted promptly.

He immediately organized and dispatched a volunteer corps under Chartres Brew, head of the Colonial Police. This force started from New Westminster. Next, he ordered Judge Cox to leave his post at Alexandria, on the upper Fraser, and, with a number of chosen men, scour the Chilcotin country for the renegades and bring them to justice. Judge Cox was well qualified to carry out this undertaking. He was skilful in handling men and never hesitated to adopt the most unorthodox means to carry out the task in hand.

Judge Cox and Mr. Brew realized that although their arrival brought a measure of relief to the terrified settlers, there was danger of further massacres as long as those Indians responsible for the uprising were free. They must be caught and no stone must be left unturned in the search. Governor Seymour felt the same way and decided to join personally in the hunt.

It was no easy task for the search parties. The rough nature of the country and lack of means of transportation made access to the outlaws' hide-outs impossible. The search parties were new to the country and had to search blindly trails which the Indians knew well. The white men had to burden themselves with supplies while the Indians lived off the land and could travel lightly.

They led the searchers, ever in danger of ambush, into treacherous, rock-strewn country and then seemed to disappear into thin air. Food supplies began to give out, yet the search must go on. Volunteer reinforcements joined in the hunt but the assassins also gained reinforcements as time passed. It seemed that the whole Chilcotin tribe, from the summit of the Cascade Mountains to the beaches of the Fraser River, was united in the uprising.

The white men made their headquarters in a log fort on a hill overlooking Benshee Lake. Rations were slim as food became alarmingly low and Brew and Cox turned their attention to the Indians who had refused to join the insurgents. The chief of the eastern branch of the Chilcotins, who had taken no part in the massacres, was approached and Governor Seymour and his two chief assistants made every effort to gain his support. But neither he nor his people would betray the whereabouts of

Klattassin and his followers. Valuable time was wasted in visiting small native villages and trying to get information. They found that some were willing to help if the hunt was allowed to turn into a series of native vendettas. But Governor Seymour had no intention of allowing this to happen.

Rumours of the renegades' plans for further attacks spread from one lonely ranch to another, causing the owners to spend long nights behind barred windows and doors waiting in terror for the worst to happen.

One delay after another hindered the searchers, yet they kept on doggedly. They spread out, slowly circling their prey. One night one of the parties had stopped to make camp when some native women and children joined them. Here was the opportunity for Judge Cox to put his shrewd knowledge of the Indian mind to good use. He quickly ordered food placed before the visitors and then ignored them while they ravenously finished every morsel. Later he talked kindly to them but allowed them to leave without questioning them. He knew that word would soon spread of his hospitality and the women would tell how they had left freely. This proved true and soon others, even a few men, wandered into the searchers' camp. It was not long before these Indians began to question each other as to the wisdom of their hot-headed chief. Judge Cox worked astutely to win the friendship and confidence of these people.

His efforts were rewarded on the day when the chief of the eastern branch of the Chilcotin Indians finally agreed to meet Governor Seymour. He sent word that he would meet him at the log fort on Benshee Lake. The white men were jubilant at this new turn of events. The meeting would break the back of the rebellion.

Governor Seymour and Judge Cox carried off the parley with such tact and strength of purpose that they managed to win the respect and loyalty of the chief. He left happy with a reward for his action.

Other chiefs soon heard of this and began to realize what they would lose if they did not do the same. Klattassin had become tiresome to them with his boasting and they began to see that his cause was a losing one. Sooner or later the searching parties would find their quarry and they feared the consequent punishment. To surrender now might mean a bargaining power at least. So, one after another, they deserted Klattassin and came to the fort on the hill.

Klattassin heard of this in his hidden refuge and realized that his cause was lost. He knew his former friends would sooner or later betray his whereabouts to Governor Seymour. He, and those followers who were still loyal to him, had been hounded until they were forced to flee further and further from their sources of food. They would soon have to surrender or starve. Klattassin surrendered.

Governor Seymour called a meeting of the Chilcotins and spoke to the large crowd gathered to hear his verdict. He looked at the dark eyes upturned to him, some sullen and resentful, others hopeful. In a loud, firm voice he told them that those who took part in the massacres would be given a fair trial, according to the white man's law. If found guilty, they would pay the supreme penalty. Those who had "clean hearts" would be taken back into the great white family and treated fairly. They were his friends and could return to their families. The white men living among them would forget in time and they would all work together in trust and friendship. The Indians must place confidence in their white neighbours.

While he spoke Governor Seymour decided to keep in

mind when he returned to Victoria the wrongs these Indians
had felt were done to them. Where these wrongs existed,
they would be eliminated so that a hot-headed leader could
not again lead his people astray.

Klattassin stood and listened to the white man's words.
His eyes flashed with anger as he saw the effect they were
having on those around him. He realized how futile his
hopes were of keeping men, like the one who was speaking,
out of his country. The white man was telling of events
which were to come when more settlers arrived to live
peacefully in the Chilcotin. He stirred restlessly, then spat
angrily on the ground. He knew what his fate was to be.

He was right. Just six months after he started on the war-
path Chief Klattassin and his guilty followers were hanged.

Home Is Where the Heart Is

A Story of Early Days in the Royal City, New Westminster

The tocsin sounded a shrill alarm from the Hyack tower, waking young and old from their sleep. The men of New Westminster's volunteer fire-brigade hurried into their clothes and raced for the fire-hall.

Amy Power stood at the window and watched Hugh, her husband, buttoning his tunic as he ran up the street. She turned as he disappeared from sight and sat down on the bed, wondering where the fire was and hoping it was not anyone's home.

Her thoughts turned back to the day, eleven years before, when she and Hugh arrived in Queensborough with Captain Luard's detachment of the Royal Engineers. It had been a long, wearying journey from England but the "Immigrant Soldiers", as they were nicknamed, did their best to liven the trip for the wives and children who accompanied them.

They were disappointed indeed when they arrived at Queensborough and found no proper camp waiting for them. However, the men pitched in and hurriedly erected shelters and the kindly captain of a Hudson's Bay brigantine lying at anchor, took aboard some of the mothers and children. Amy had not minded the hardships she had to face and found plenty to do when her own home was finally built.

The men of the Engineers made a comfortable settlement out of a handful of wooden buildings and their original camp. As the years passed, more settlers arrived and it became an important young city. The pioneers were very proud indeed when Queen Victoria, at their request, chose a new name for Queensborough. By Royal Proclamation she not only changed the name to New Westminster but also proclaimed it, "A Royal City and Capital of British Columbia."

Amy, as well as the other wives of the Royal Engineers, proudly considered their menfolk the builders of New Westminster. When a miner or merchant's wife dared question their claim they would ask, "Isn't it true that Sapperton was named for the Sappers of our detachment?"

The five years before the Royal Engineers disbanded were a mixture of happy, exciting days and lonely ones for the wives. They were alone while the men were off building the Cariboo Road, acting as guards for shipments of gold from the mining camps, quelling Indian uprisings and keeping order among the miners. But these hardy women did not waste time on self-pity. Their time was spent on community efforts.

When the "Emigrant Soldiers" disbanded they were offered their choice of land grants or passage home. Only a few returned to England. Amy and Hugh were among the first to accept the grant and they built a new home in a grove of trees with a view of the river. In time their farm prospered and they became contented farmers.

The city grew and the men realized they needed a fire-brigade. They formed a volunteer one. They called it the "Hyacks", the Chinook word for, "Hurry Up". They paid for their own uniforms and fire-fighting equipment. They were conscious of the prestige of this capital city of the new Province of British Columbia, so chose very impressive uniforms. A jaunty cap topped gay, scarlet tunics with black velvet collars and cuffs, worn over well-creased dark trousers. The Hyacks became the male social leaders of the town. They gave very impressive balls and organized theatrical and musical groups. Their band always drew large crowds to concerts.

As Amy sat on the bed thinking of all these things, Hugh reached the fire-hall. He found the team of horses had already been harnessed to the steam fire-wagon and the fire lit under the boiler. Hugh looked at it and hoped it would burn brighter and faster than the one they were going to and so build up a good pressure before they reached the scene. He took his place with the other men and they were off. The horses tore down the main street, urged on by the brass bell clanging its warning to the people who were also running to the fire.

When they arrived, they found the owners of the small house which was ablaze, working vainly to control the flames. The Hyacks barely waited for the horses to be pulled to a stop before they started unreeling the hose and working the hand pump. Then, when they found they could not save the house, they turned their attention to the furniture and dragged it outside. In the meantime friends and neighbours were trying to save the barn and out-buildings.

Later, when only the charred ruins of the house remained and nothing more could be done, Hugh joined the small group gathered around the owners. Mary and Paul Cornish had travelled to Queensborough on the boat with Amy and

Hugh. Paul had also accepted a grant of land and farmed it. Mary, unlike Amy, had not wanted to stay and tried desperately to persuade her husband to take her back to England. Hugh realized how she would feel now that they had lost their home. He said to her,

"Mary, come and stay with us, there is plenty of room, and Amy will be very happy having you with us."

A slight, fair-haired girl of twelve joined them, saying to her mother:

"Mummie, the horses and cows all stayed right in the meadow. They are safe."

Her mother seemed too stunned to hear so Hugh spoke to her husband:

"Take Mary and Angela to our house, Paul. Tell Amy I'll be home shortly. Hurry and get Mary away from here, she is taking this very hard."

"You're right Hugh. I won't try to say how much I appreciate your kindness. I'm fraid Mary won't stay here now, she'll want to go back home as soon as possible." This seemed to worry Paul more than the loss of his house. Hugh nodded, then turned away to join his companions who were winding up the hose and preparing to leave.

When he returned home he found his wife trying to persuade her guests to eat breakfast but with little success. He joined them at the table and as Amy poured his tea she said,

"I'm so glad you are going to stay with us, Mary. It is years since we have had a real visit together."

"I appreciate what you are doing Amy but Angela and I won't stay with you very long," she looked at her husband. "We are going back to England as soon as it can be arranged. Paul can join us when he has sold up whatever is left from the fire."

"What would I do in England?" asked Paul.

"You'll go into your father's office, of course. He wanted you to go into his business with him but you foolishly insisted upon joining the Royal Engineers and coming to this outlandish country." Her voice ended on a shrill note.

Hugh caught Paul's eye and shook his head. Amy spoke quickly to Angela, "Shall we go upstairs and fix up the rooms for your Mummie and Daddy and yourself? You will have my sewing room for your very own. It will be so nice having a young girl with us." She stood up. "Mary, you are so fortunate having a daughter."

"Yes, but not in having to bring her up here with nothing ahead of her except hard work." Mary's voice was bitter.

"Now, Mary," Hugh smiled at her. "The Hyacks have a theatrical group you can join and we are going to put on a light opera in a few months' time."

"Amateur music and theatricals are poor substitutes for what we are missing in the way of culture," was her reply.

Amy started for the door. "Come with me Mary and lie down. You need a rest after what you have been through." Mary did not answer but followed her from the room.

The next few weeks passed quickly for everyone except Mary. She seemed to have no interest whatever in what was happening around her. She refused to be roused by her husband and daughter's efforts and only expressed one wish . . . to leave New Westminster and go "home". Her husband gave in finally and started making plans for her departure.

But Amy told him one night of a plan and convinced him that it would change Mary's attitude. In the following days Mary seemed unaware of her hostess' absence and an air of mysterious excitement shared by her daughter and the others as they whispered on their return in the evenings.

When Angela did not come home after school Mary didn't reprimand her but spoke only of the day when they would leave "this dreadful place". She ignored Angela's protest, "Mummie, it is nice here. I don't want to leave all our friends."

It was a soft, warm April day when Amy announced at breakfast, "Mary you are coming with us for a drive. Hugh is taking the day off and is now harnessing the horses to the democrat, so hurry and get ready." Amy added gayly, "We have declared today a holiday for Angela too and she is coming with us."

"I can't think whatever for . . . why would we want to drive anywhere today?" '

"Nonsense, Mary. It is time we had a holiday, so no more protests. Come along and get ready." She firmly overruled her guest and hurried her upstairs.

Later, Angela trying to suppress excitement, chattered incessantly until her mother remarked, "I have never seen you act this way about anything. Whatever is this all about?"

"Oh, Mummie, don't spoil everything by being so cross."

There was silence as they drove along until Mary exclaimed, "Why, this is the road to our place!"

'Yes," Hugh winked at his wife, "I'm going to take the path down to the river."

Mary did not speak again until Hugh finally stopped the horses beside a wire fence.

"Everyone gets out and walks from here," Angela sang out excitedly.

They walked until they turned a corner and Mary stopped and stared . . . The others watched her anxiously until finally she said,

"Why this *is* our place . . . but, Oh!" She could not say more. She was speechless as she stared at the miracle ahead of her. A trim, well-built house stood where she had last seen the ruins of her home. Smoke curled lazily from a stone chimney and curtains hung crisply at shining windows.

Hugh grabbed her arm saying, "Don't stand there and stare. Come along and see your new house." He hurried her forward and opening the door, gently pushed her towards her husband who stood waiting for her. The door to the sittingroom opened and a group of friends shouted happily, "Welcome home, Mary." Her eyes filled with tears and she was unable to speak. She saw through an open door a table laden with food on a snowy white cloth. Someone led her into the room and to the chair drawn up to a blazing fireplace. She sat down and all she could say was, "Oh, my goodness," over and over again until the room almost rocked with the laughter of her friends. Her amazement gave way to a smile and a moment later she joined in the happy laughter.

Luncheon was a merry one and when it was finished Amy said to her: "Come along Mary and see the other rooms."

Two bedrooms were furnished completely, even to hand-embroidered spreads on the beds. The kitchen gleamed from the fire in a shiny, new stove behind which hung bright pots and other cooking-utensils; cups and saucers and other dishes were neatly arranged in a large cupboard. Even freshly cleaned lamps stood ready to be lighted.

They finally returned to the sitting-room and found the others had slipped away, leaving only Hugh and Amy to hear her grateful thanks. Angela said to her,

"Mummie, isn't this wonderful . . . we were all working so hard and you never guessed our secret. The men built the house and most of the furniture and I helped the ladies with the sewing. Aunt Amy has taught me to sew."

"Yes, it is indeed wonderful, Angela. What good friends! How can I ever thank them?" Mary's voice trembled.

"You can thank us by staying here and being happy," replied Hugh.

"There's another wonderful surprise," Angela's eyes shone happily. "The Hyacks are going to help us have a May Day celebration. It is to be exactly like the ones you have told me about so often, the times when you were young and danced on the village green . . . remember . . . the May Pole Dance? Well, Uncle Hugh says the Hyacks decided that because you and the other ladies were missing the May Day festivities so much, they were going to start having them here."

Mary looked at her husband, who said, "It is true, we have made all the plans."

"I am going to be a Maid of Honour and Helen McColl is to be May Queen, the first one in New Westminster. Isn't that lovely?" Angela laughed, "next year I might be Queen of the May."

"I remember when I was a little girl like you, I was once a May Queen." Mary spoke to her husband. "I don't know what to say to you, Paul. I have been behaving dreadfully . . . but I can truthfully say I want to stay here now. All these good friends have done so very, very much for us."

Amy stood up, "Well, I'm sure Colonel Moody hardly thought all this would happen when he chose New Westminster as the site for a new city which was to be the first capital of British Columbia."

"No, nor did the Hyacks think when they formed a fire-brigade that they would be decking their fire-engine with flowers to use as a May Queen's throne." Hugh smiled at Angela.

Later, when Amy and Hugh had left and Angela was in bed, Mary and Paul sat by the fire and Mary said softly,

"We will never find better friends anywhere, Paul. This is really our home now."

Paul smiled as he reached for her hand, "Always remember, my dear, home is where the heart is."

The Taming of Wildhorse

The Story of a Mining Camp in the Kootenays.

It was a warm, sunny day and a band of wild horses grazed by a creek in the east Kootenay country. They neighed in fright, then pounded away as two trappers approached them.

The men came in search of gold in the creek bed. They had met an Indian friend on the trail a few days before and he had shown them a skin poke full of gold dust and nuggets. In answer to their excited questions he replied, "Gold, plenty gold in creek bed," and generously told them how to find the creek.

When they arrived, they barely noticed the wild horses, but hurried to make camp and set to work panning for the gold. By evening, exhausted but triumphant, they had taken enough dust out of the creek to know that they had made a rich strike.

"It won't be long before word of this gets out," said one of them.

"No indeed," said the other. "When we go to the trading post for supplies it'll soon leak out. Guess we'd better get ready for the rush before that crowd around Colville and Walla Walla gets here." His companion nodded and the two men finished their meal in silence.

Each knew what the other was thinking . . . about the men who would flock into this lonely country, determined to find their fortune. There would be old prospectors who followed the news of every gold strike, always hoping this would be "it". The men and women, who lived off them when they struck it rich, would come too, confidence men, dance hall girls, gamblers. Walla Wala, just across the border, was the supply centre of the miners who had come to Canada from California, Idaho and Montana. The man who ran the nearest Hudson's Bay trading post also went to Walla Walla or Fort Colville from time to time. He would tell of the new strike and a mad rush would be certain to follow.

The fire burned low and the two trappers prepared to turn in. "Guess we better give this place a name," said one.

'What about calling it after them wild horses we saw grazing by the creek this afternoon when we arrived?" asked his companion. "Them cayuses will come in mighty handy for packin' in stuff and them bein' here shows there's feed for animals in these hills."

His friend agreed and so a new mining camp was born and became known as Wild Horse. The expected happened and, soon the small camp mushroomed into a booming, rowdy mining town. The board sidewalk of the single street was faced with hastily thrown up buildings to be used as stores, dance halls, saloons and gambling joints. Miners' cabins replaced tents. Most of the log cabins had dirt floors, the few with floors being regarded as very superior. Open fireplaces were used for cooking and heating; furnishings were home-made benches, tables and bunks. Fir or pine boughs with rough blankets thrown over them made the miners' beds. Winters were long in Wild Horse, so the cabins were warmly chinked against the cold and baked clay chimneys were stoutly built. These hardy out-door men lived on salt pork, beans, flap jacks, tea and coffee, with tobacco a necessity for most. They all dressed alike; flannel shirts with trousers tucked into high boots and broad-brimmed hats framing faces generally covered by beards.

The first year of the gold rush tested the stamina of the miners. Those who could not stand the long hours of shovelling heavy, wet dirt, or panning in the creek beds gave up and drifted away, or took jobs in town. That winter it was impossible to bring in supplies over frozen trails. Many experienced hardships and hunger until spring came and with it the pack-trains. Food was eagerly pounced upon even at the exorbitant prices asked and everyone paid for it in gold dust and nuggets.

Stories about those days in Wild Horse are based mostly on hear-say because the official records were burned. It was not an accidental fire, but one typical of the feverish desire for gold wherever it could be found. One day rumours flew about that a rich vein of gold lay under the cabin used as the official government building. That night a group of men worked swiftly in the dark; flames roared, and the next morning the cabin was in ashes, everything in it destroyed. At dawn men were seen digging furiously. The rumour was well founded. They found gold but all official records were burned in the fire.

There were thrifty as well as free-spending groups in the mining town. The former, as well as the merchants, took their gold dust and nuggets across the border to Walla Walla. A man named Dorsey Baker, ran a trading post there and was the only one in that part of the country who owned a safe. He would take the poke offered by each miner who came to him, write his name on it and toss it into the safe, without bothering to give a receipt. When the safe was full he threw the over-flow into a nail keg. This was the lowly beginning of the Boyd-Baker National Bank of Walla Walla. A Roman Catholic church and school were built at Wild Horse and the hard-working priest tried his best to overcome the bad influences of the fast-growing camp.

There was of course a rowdy element among the miners and some "bad men" with well-notched guns. Confidence men drifted into camp well supplied with smooth means of separating the gullible man from his wealth. Each man was a law unto himself, restraint came only from the wiser and stronger men who formed the miners' courts. Saturday nights were spent in uproarious celebrations. Pale faced gamblers and painted, perfumed dance hall girls waited to empty the miners' brimming pokes when they arrived from creek or hill.

There were so many Americans in the town that the Fourth of July was the excuse for a noisy celebration. One of the Americans was known for his hot temper and quick finger on the trigger of his gun. He was called Yeast Powder Bill. On one Fourth of July, Bill came in from his cabin early in the day and by night-time was well on in his celebration. He was standing by the bar in one of the saloons boasting about the fortune he was going to make when someone jostled his elbow and a gruff voice told him to, shut up.

Yeast Powder Bill's famous temper flared and instantly his gun was in his hand. He fired but his shot went wild. His opponent returned the fire and Yeast Powder Bill was minus a finger. Ignoring his wounded hand he took careful aim and fired again. His victim crashed to the floor. Bill swayed drunkenly as he waited for the other to get up. He did not realize he had killed him until he was grabbed by rough hands and taken to a cabin where he was locked up for the night. Next morning he was tried by a miners' jury and found guilty. He was warned to get out of camp within the hour. Barely five minutes later his horse's hoof-beats were heard pounding furiously into the distance and one of the jurymen remarked,

"Guess we seen the last of Bill. He'll head back to the States and more'n likely that temper of his'll get him into worse trouble than this."

In the opinion of his friends in Wild Horse, Yeast Powder Bill had after all only killed a man during a drunken celebration.

But one man did not take matters so lightly when he rode into town one day, accompanied by a constable. John Haynes had been sent to represent the government, collect revenues, and try to stop lawlessness. He had barely settled down to his duties before he was faced with a serious situation.

An outlaw, wanted by the police of many cities, had arrived in the new mining town a short time before. Hiding there, he preyed on the easy-going, generous miners. Then he made the serious mistake of stealing two horses from a prospector. The owner of the animals hurried to Mr. Haynes demanding that he arrest the thief and get back the horses. John Haynes sent for the outlaw but he had disappeared and the constable was sent to find him. He found him but before he could arrest him, the outlaw drew his gun and killed him.

When the murdered man's body was found and brought back to town every miner left his claim. A posse was quickly formed and the men rode off to get their man and make him pay for his crime. Miners' law acted swiftly. From their point of view, the worst crime the outlaw had committed was stealing the horses. At that time, in that isolated country, a man could easily starve to death if he lost his horse. Only these pack animals could travel over the rough trails and hills, and the supplies they carried meant the difference between life and death to the miners. So a horse-thief was the lowest type of criminal.

The search was long and difficult. It led the posse across the border into Idaho where, in a wild and lonely spot, they found their man. They did not bother to take him back to Wild Horse. They looked about them at the many trees. Their leader pointed to one.

"This will do," he said grimly. It was a tree suitable for a hanging. The prisoner knew better than to draw his gun this time and pleading did not do him any good. When the stern-faced men left him, he had paid the final penalty for both horse-stealing and murder.

Mr. Haynes heard about the hanging but he was powerless. Indeed he was soon impressed by the miners' honesty. In less than two months he collected $16,000 from them in revenues. It was in gold, weighing around seventy-five pounds. He put it into a battered old suitcase and pushed it under the bunk in his cabin. It was still there when the Hon. Arthur Birch, Colonial Secretary, arrived in Wild Horse on an inspection trip. The good man was horrified when he saw this careless treatment of gold. He took it with him on his return to Victoria. The old suitcase, bulging with gold, was the first shipment to go direct from the Rocky Mountains to the coast in the days when British Columbia was a colony.

As time passed the miners spent recklessly though their

sprees grew milder. One Saturday night a man called Fancy
Jack walked into a saloon with some companions, all in a
hilarious state. They pushed their way through the crowd
up to the bar. Jack ordered the bartender to "set 'em up"
in the grand manner. He insisted that everyone in the
room must drink with him. He was laughing loudly at one
of his own jokes when he noticed the man next to him
push away the glass which the bartender had placed in
front of him. Fancy Jack showed that he was hurt by this
refusal of his generosity. He watched the man in silence
for a moment, then picking up the glass tried to force him
to drink from it. This so annoyed the other that he told
Jack what he thought of him in no uncertain terms and
walked out of the saloon. His companions laughed as they
saw the injured expression on the face of their drunken
host. The latter's sense of injury turned quickly to rage
and he threw the glass and it's contents at the man nearest
him, pulled his poke from his pocket, opened it, and
brought out a fistful of nuggets. With a single heave, he
threw them at the bottles of liquor standing on a shelf
behind the bar. The bartender ducked but the huge mirror
behind him shattered when the nuggets crashed into it.
Fancy Jack swayed as he looked bleary-eyed around him,
then muttering that his night's fun had been spoiled, he
left.

Next morning, sober and repentent, he returned and
without a word threw a bag of gold dust on the bar.
He told the astounded bartender that he knew the mirror
he had broken would be hard to replace. He added that he
hoped the gold dust would pay for the damage he had done
the night before. He did not ask for the return of his nuggets
he had thrown at the mirror, nor did the bartender offer
to give them back.

The years passed and claims petered out; many miners left Wild Horse. The Indians in the East Kootenay country were becoming more and more antagonistic towards the white men who were encroaching on their hunting and camping grounds. They felt particularly hostile towards the surveyors who came to survey land that the red men considered their own. Worse still, their chief learned one day, that land was to be blocked out for Indian reservations. He protested hotly but the survey work went on. The Indians tried to discourage this by pulling up stakes as quickly as the surveyors got them into the ground. The miners who remained around Wild Horse were equally unpopular but for a different reason. The natives had expected them to bring them trade goods as had the fur-traders but the miners ignored the Indians and kept to themselves.

One morning the people of Wild Horse woke up to discover that two miners had been murdered. They had been working their claim in an isolated spot when they were attacked. A wandering prospector found their bodies and hurried to town to report the murders. Everyone was up in arms and a thorough investigation was made. It was discovered that two Indians had quarreled with the dead men. They were suspected of the crime.

Meantime the Indians had disappeared and for a long time could not be found for questioning. Their tribesmen hid them but one of them was finally caught and put into jail. Almost immediately their chief rode into Wildhorse followed by a large number of his tribe, armed and ready for trouble. They surrounded the jail and, before anyone could stop them, freed the prisoner. Next, the chief inso-lently ordered the constable and chief surveyor to leave the country at once.

The miners and the few settlers knew that they were terribly out-numbered by the natives. To add to their alarm they heard that a settler, who owned the land where the city of Cranbrook now stands, was threatened and ordered off his property by Indians. A messenger was sent to Victoria asking the Government to help them.

The Government answered by sending Major Sam Steele of the North West Mounted Police with a detachment of one hundred men to Wildhorse. Major Steele sent at once for the chief and his tribesmen. The haughty chief decided he had better obey but listened coldly to the white man as he spoke.

"I have not come to cause you trouble. You must control your men and behave properly and all will be well; but from now on the North West Mounted Police will make sure that you pay for your misdeeds."

The chief looked keenly at the tall man in the impressive uniform, scarlet jacket with shining brass buttons, and knew that he meant every word he said. He stood for a moment in awed silence then turned and spoke sharply to his warriors. Some muttered sullenly but all followed him when he rode off. The trouble was ended.

When the gold petered out the miners drifted away to seek their fortunes elsewhere. But Wildhorse refused to die without a final burst of notoriety. Overnight, it became a centre of political intrigue with worried politicians at Victoria shaking their heads at the mention of its name.

In its heyday Wildhorse was represented by two members of parliament. Its dying condition was overlooked at Victoria and the time rolled around for another election to find only eleven voters left there. Worse still, the parties contending for power were so evenly divided that two members from Wildhorse might very well mean victory or defeat for either of them.

A check revealed that of the eleven voters five were known supporters of one party; five were equally staunch supporters of the other. The political leanings of the eleventh, if any, were a mystery.

The latter was an old prospector living alone in his cabin by a deserted claim. Hope of striking it rich had, like himself, faded with the years. His remaining ambition was to maintain himself in a state of semi-intoxication in which the realities of the present gave way to hazy dreams of the past. Of late this had become more and more difficult, for financial reasons.

He was in a state of temporary sobriety when, a few days before the election, he was visited by a stranger from Victoria. His visitor had been delegated to guide the old man towards the right political opinions. The latter smoked in silence, faded eyes staring at the wall, until his guest's flow of rhetoric faltered. Then, seizing his opportunity, he slyly drawled,

"Perhaps after all them words you should have a mite o' something to wet yer whistle, son. I could do with a drop myself."

The stranger took the hint and was back shortly with a bottle.

The next day a second visitor, a supporter of the rival political party, appeared and a similar interview took place. At least the result was the same.

Alternately the two visitors cultivated the old man's favour. Each tried to win him over as they satisfied his thirst. His clouded senses remained fixed on one thing. As long as he misunderstood their arguments and gave no promises, the free liquor continued to flow. He had hit pay-dirt at last.

Election day arrived. The clock in the polling centre ticked away but there was no sign of the eleventh voter. Closing time was approaching when a delegation rushed off to find him. They pounded furiously on the cabin door but there was no response. Bursting in, they found the old man and his two guests stretched out, dead to the world. Their snores in three ascending keys was the only sign of life. Pails of icy water poured over them, in disgust, failed to rouse them.

The pole closed and the all-important voter slept on. The vote was a tie.

Consternation reigned in Victoria when it was realized that another election must be held at Wildhorse. This time more responsible agents were on the job. Their instructions had been specific. No matter for whom his vote might be cast, the old man must mark his ballot.

The ancient prospector, however, would not yield his advantage except for a liquid price. Having tasted the rewards of power he demanded the privilege due his position. So free liquor still flowed his way but a careful rationing on the night before the election produced results. The now notorious voter staggered, with help, into the polling booth and placed a shaky cross on a ballot.

The whole Province heard with relief that the tie was broken. But the remaining citizens of Wildhorse learned to their horror that it had taken all the liquor in their community to elect a new government at Victoria.

Wildhorse had reached the end of its hectic career. In time, the last cabin was abandoned and wild horses again grazed in solitude around the crumbling remains of another ghost town in the Kootenays.

this was waived, even though the organizers of the party learned to their utter astonishment that another addition to the Schubert family was expected in some five months. The twenty-eight year old mother scoffed at their fears and protests and assured them that they would reach their destination long before the birth of her fourth child.

Before the Overlanders started out on the fifth of June, everything possible had been done for the comfort of Mrs. Schubert and her children. A cow was teamed with an ox and hitched to a covered light wagon inside which were all the family's possessions. The children would need milk.

Sometimes from the seat of the wagon, sometimes riding her horse by its side, Catherine watched over her family and their possessions. Mary and Augustus most of the time rode comfortably in two basket cradles hanging across the back of a horse. Two-year-old James usually rode with his father or, at times with his father's friend, Peter McIntyre. As they journeyed on, Catherine dreamed of the future and the new home they would have when the creek beds of the Cariboo yielded a fortune in gold.

It was a very impressive sight as the caravan set out from Fort Garry. Ninety-seven Red River carts and one hundred and ten animals passed through the gates as the people of the Fort cheered and shouted farewell and God-speed. The experiences of earlier California-bound wagon trains helped to guide the Overlanders in their organization. They travelled in regional groups, such as the Ottawa group and the Red River group, which stayed together as far as possible, especially when camping at night. In this way each group was responsible, to a degree, for the safety of its own people. The captain and his counsellors, the latter representing various groups, were responsible for the over-all welfare of the caravan. If a breakdown occurred the owner of the disabled cart must turn out to make his repairs and, when he rejoined the cavalcade, he must take his place at the end of the line so as not to hinder the progress of the party.

The time came when Catherine's dreams seemed to fade, though they never died in spite of trials and dangers. When water and food became scarce, when streams they had hoped to find turned out to be nothing but stagnant pools, and food could not be supplemented as they had hoped by game, it was her cheery optimism and her practical way of "making do" that encouraged the weary men. She never complained, nor would she admit discomfort owing to her condition.

The time came when, first the oxen and then the horses, had to be sacrificed for food. Everyone had to walk, laden with what they could carry. Catherine, not only kept up with the men, but helped her two older children while her husband and McIntyre took turns in carrying the youngest. She carried on ignoring the fact that the journey was taking far longer than they had expected. At last they reached the Rockies.

Toiling through the mountain forest was a back-breaking task, and though food supplies were almost gone, they dared not delay to hunt game, for the evenings were already chilly and signs of approaching winter began to appear. Then came a day when a difficult decision had to be made. After months of sharing good and bad fortune, they must separate into two parties, one to go ahead more rapidly than the other. How were they to determine who should go first? One thing was unanimously agreed. Mrs. Schubert must get to Kamloops so that she might have suitable care when her baby was born.

The small party, which included the Schuberts, struggled doggedly forward. Then one day they noticed trees with the bark chipped in a peculiar manner. Following this blazed trail, they came upon a band of Indians who greeted them in the friendliest fashion. These natives not only provided food but offered them dug-out canoes and helped them build rafts. While the work of felling trees and building rafts went on, Mrs. Schubert had a very welcome rest. The Indian women vied with one another in doing their utmost for her and the children. They even provided her with a fur robe for her journey downstream.

At the earliest possible moment the party started off. Mr. Schubert and the two older children were on one of the rafts and Mrs. Schubert with the youngest child in a dug-out with one of the men. She tried to settle back comfortably but her anxious eyes were constantly strained on the raft ahead.

The man with her tried in a friendly way to divert her attention by pointing out interesting bits of scenery. Catherine smiled gratefully at him and was chiding herself for her foolish anxiety when suddenly she heard shouts ahead. She started to jump to her feet but her companion pulled her down with a stern, "Keep still or you'll upset us." The poor woman trembled as she sank back and stared at the raft which was turning and spinning like a top. She could hear the terrified screams of her children as they called her name. Then, before her horrified eyes, the raft tilted in the air and turned over. Excited voices mingled with the sound of splintering wood as it crashed on a submerged rock.

The distracted mother tried once more to rise to her feet but a strong hand held her down. She closed her eyes and sat motionless with fear. But cheering voices caused her to open her eyes again. Her lips moved in silent prayer. At last she found courage to look across the water to where the raft had been but a moment before.

Her husband was in the water and was holding their small daughter's head clear of it; another man held young

Augustus who was sputtering in his efforts to call to her. A canoe moved quickly towards the two men with their small burdens, and then another, and the children were lifted to safety.

It was not long after this incident, when quieter water was reached, Catherine's indomitable spirit asserted itself once more. She insisted on joining her family and continuing with them on another raft. "Look what happens when I leave them alone," she remarked.

Difficult times continued and once more food ran low. They came to a deserted village near the river and decided to land in the hope of finding something to eat. Mrs. Schubert gathered her little brood together and with the others set off towards the village. They met an old native woman who shouted at them in a shrill voice, motioning them to hurry back to the water. Mrs. Schubert ignored these warnings and walked firmly forward. She had almost reached the old woman when one of the men ran back from the dwellings shouting, "Smallpox!" An epidemic had wiped out the village and the old woman was the only one who had escaped the dread scourge.

For a moment Mrs. Schubert looked at her children and hesitated. Then she pointed and called, "Potatoes! A whole field of them."

Before anyone could stop her she hurried forward, taking care to keep well away from the old woman, who stared at her in speechless wonder. She examined the field and then, straightening up, she called to the men to come and dig them. Nothing could persuade her that the potatoes were tainted or would be harmful to eat. Their desperate need drove the men to obey her command and soon a goodly supply was gathered. She waved the thanks of the party to the old woman, who waved back in a friendly manner as she stood gazing after them until they disappeared from view.

Anxiety for Mrs. Schubert grew each day of their trip down the Thompson River. Everyone knew it was a race for time.

It was evening when one of the men pointed shorewards and shouted, "Fort Kamloops!" Wild cheers followed his words and Mrs. Schubert murmured a prayer of thanks for the safe ending of her journey.

When the people of the Fort hurried down to the water's edge they could hardly believe their eyes when they saw the three small children who had made that incredible journey. There was an awed silence when Mrs. Schubert was helped ashore. She was too exhausted to make even the short trip to the Fort. So she was placed in the care of an elderly Indian woman who hurried her to her nearby tent.

The Overlanders had undertaken their long, dangerous journey with one thought in mind only—gold. But during their first few hours in Fort Kamloops gold was far from their thoughts. Their anxiety was soon relieved, however, when the motherly Indian woman appeared carrying a tiny bundle. A loud wail coming from it announced that the first white girl had been born in Kamloops. Catherine Schubert's long ordeal was over. The lone woman of the Overlanders had triumphantly reached her goal.

Beefsteak on the Hoof

A Cattle Drive Over the Old Canyon Road

The ranch house stood in a grove of trees near the head of Nicola Lake. The little stream, swollen by the spring freshets, chattered its way noisily past the back door. The rolling grasslands on either side narrowed on the valley floor and rose in benches to the foot of the mountain barriers to the east and west.

Darkness still enveloped the scene one spring morning long ago. The faint calls of water fowl drifted across the lake and from the corrals came the subdued sounds of restless cattle. Suddenly lights twinkled on in the ranch house and in the nearby quarters of the cattle hands.

An hour later, as spring sunshine flooded above the eastern ramparts and spilled over the valley, the peace of early morning gave way to feverish activity. A great herd of cattle rounded up during the preceding days, moved out of the corrals onto the lake shore road under the guidance of skilled cowhands. As the last of them headed southward the rattling chuckwagon took up its accustomed place at the rear of the procession. Heralded by the shouting of the cowboys and the bawling of the protesting steers, the first cattle drive of the year across the mountains to far-off Yale was on.

As it got under way the owner of the ranch, Sam Moore, rode back to the house. He and his wife, Mary, tiptoed up to the room where their two children slept. Sam smiled as each in turn having kissed him and murmured a sleepy goodbye, was back in the Land of Nod before their parents were out of the room.

"Healthy little beggars, eh, Mary?" he commented as they came to the front door.

Moments later from his saddle Sam looked down at his wife as he said, "Well, goodbye, Mary. I'll be back inside of a month if all goes well. Hope you will not be too lonely."

"Goodbye, Sam, and do take care of yourself. Don't worry about me or the children. We'll be all right. Anyway, John is not far away."

"I'm glad that brother of mine isn't making the drive with us this trip, so there'll be someone here to look after you. But I must be off, dear."

His wife smiled up bravely at her tall, handsome husband as he spoke. She watched him whirl his horse and gallop towards the road. As he passed through the gate he turned and waved. Her answering wave was reassuring and he dug his spurs into his mount.

He rode hard down the lakeshore until a cloud of dust showed him where his herd was slowy moving forward. He would be up with them shortly. He pulled in his tough little cayuse and his thoughts turned back to Mary. She looked so small and lonely as she waved goodbye.

Had he been too hasty in taking this girl from her comfortable Ontario home and bringing her west to share his life as a pioneer rancher in the Nicola Valley? Yet she seemed to love the country and their life together. And now that the children had come along she could never be really lonely. His herds of cattle were growing. The price of beef was good. A few more years and they would be well off. Meantime more settlers were straggling into their lovely valley and it was certain that a railway, running through Kamloops forty odd miles away, would some day soon link them with both eastern Canada and the Pacific Coast.

He urged his horse into a gallop and a few moments later pulled up beside the chuck-wagon.

"Goin' to be a dandy day, boss. Sure hope this weather holds out 'til we get to Yale." The driver, who was also the cook for the outfit, leaned from his seat as he spoke.

"Yes, Dan . . . so do I. But it's pretty warm for this time of year. If the water's too high along the trail we may have to use your wagon for a boat."

They both laughed as Sam's eyes roved over the cattle ahead of them. They were in prime condition. Nicola Valley bunch-grass was wonderful feed. The long drive over the mountains would take some of the fat off their ribs but, even at that, they should arrive at the Coast in good shape.

Sam rode past the cowboy ahead of the wagon and on past the herd with its outriders to where his foreman, Bill Forsman, led the procession with two companions. As he rode the shimmering waters of the lake caught Sam's eye and he looked towards the mountains rising from its western shore. No wonder Mary loved the beauty of this land.

As he reached his foreman's side, Sam spoke. "The streams will be mighty high, Bill. This heat will be melting the snow in the hills."

"High water ain't goin' to bother us too much, Sam. This is a husky bunch of critters—surefooted as mules. Long as we don't run into a thunderstorm in the pass, we'll make out."

Bill's drawl as he answered branded him as from south of the border. He and most of the other hands had come north with Sam when the latter had made the long trip to Wyoming to buy stock for his own ranch and that of his brother, John. That drive to the Nicola Valley had been a hard one but, thanks largely to Forsman and the other experienced hands, very few of the herd had been lost.

The men rode forward in silence and Sam's memory strayed back over the years. Tales of fortunes to be made in the Canadian West had reached his farm home in Grey County, Ontario. Their imaginations fired by these tales, he and his brother John, as mere boys, had set out for the Prairies. Travelling by way of St. Paul to Fort Garry they took up homesteads where Winnipeg now stands. Word of gold on the Fraser River and in the Cariboo had lured them on. They had joined the first expedition of "Overlanders" to cross the Rockies. Many of their original companions dropped away at the various trading posts which they passed and only the hardiest members of the expedition at last arrived at the gold fields. Sam and John Moore were among them.

For a time the brothers joined the eager throngs panning the creeks of the Cariboo for gold. Then it dawned on them that there were much surer ways of making a fortune. With the modest sums their work on the creeks had netted, they purchased a pack train and, for a time, operated it between Yale and Barkerville. They made money in this venture but competition was keen and the gold rush was well past its peak.

Fresh meat was scarce throughout the colony of British Columbia. The two Moores purchased a herd of sheep in Oregon in 1867 and started a sheep ranch on San Juan Island in the Gulf of Georgia. When as arbitrator of the boundary dispute the German Emperor gave this island to the United States, Sam and John moved into the Nicola Valley. There they established cattle ranches. The two ranches adjoined each other and their herds ranged far and wide over the bunch-grass covered benches.

When a log cabin on Sam's ranch gave way to a more substantial house, he went east to marry a boyhood sweetheart, Mary Whiteford, and brought her back by way of San Francisco and Victoria to share his fortunes. At the time of our story John was busy finishing a new house. He, too, was planning a trip to Ontario and already the date had been set for his marriage to Agnes Whiteford, a younger sister of Sam's wife.

Yes, these young pioneers were doing well. But until the much-talked-of railway came to British Columbia they would face the long trek across the mountains and down the Fraser River to Yale with their cattle. Yale was the head of navigation on the river and shipments to the growing settlements at the coast were made from there on the old, flat-bottomed stern-wheelers.

Bill Forsman brought Sam back to the present as he said, "We sure can't hurry the drive in this weather. Looks like the cook'll be the busiest man on the job."

"Yes," replied Sam, "we'll give the beasts plenty of rest. We want a little meat left on them when we get to Yale."

When they swung into the trail that followed the Nicola River, they found that Sam's fears about the rising waters had been correct. The rough trail itself demanded the utmost vigilance on the part of the cowboys. Ordinarily fording the mountrain streams did not add greatly to the dangers of a drive of this kind. But these streams were now raging torrents. In crossing them steers continually lost their footing among the boulders. When this happened lariats flicked through the air, the floundering animals were roped and dragged either to their feet or to the shore. In spite of a succession of such incidents no legs were broken and the herd was still intact as it moved slowly up the pass.

On the second day in the pass the heat was oppressive and little progress was made. A halt was called as they came to a small, grassy valley in the early afternoon. A strange restlessness was noticeable in the herd. Instead of settling down to graze, they milled about aimlessly.

The air grew still and as evening approached a strange green light flooded over the scene.

Forsman walked over to where the rancher sat smoking on a log near the chuck-wagon. "Guess we're in for that thunderstorm, Sam. Hope it hits us afore dark or we'll have real trouble."

Sam's eyes searched the sky above the surrounding peaks as he replied, "I believe you're right, Bill. We're lucky we decided it was too hot to travel further today and pulled up in this valley.'"

"Lucky's no name for it. I think we can hold the herd here all right. I'm goin' to warn the boys and get 'em lined up ready." The foreman moved off.

An hour later a flash of lightning tore a zigzag pattern across the darkening sky and a roll of thundered shattered the silence. On their heels followed a torrent of wind and rain. For moments the terrified steers milled about in senseless circles. Then suddenly, with thundering hooves, they drove towards the gap by which they had entered the valley. Their mad rush was met by the lashing whips of the shouting cowboys. The fear-maddened animals swerved about and tore in the opposite direction. Turned back again, stragglers floundered into the river or tore up the almost vertical hillside that held them prisoners.

Moments stretched into what seemed hours as in the dim light and the pouring rain the grim struggle went on, while from above the flashing lightning and rolling thunder poured new terrors over the struggling beasts.

As is the way with such mountain storms, it was all over in half an hour. A little later a full moon appeared over the black outline of the great hills and stars winked into sight to gaze down on the exhausted animals and their equally weary guardians.

A check-up the following morning showed that not one animal was missing or seriously injured. Forsman and his men had done a fine job.

"I'll certainly looked after you and the boys for last night's work, Bill, when we get to Yale." Same Moore smiled at his long-legged foreman.

"You didn't do too bad yourself, Sam. Guess this cattle hustlin's gettin' into yer blood same as the rest of us." Bill smiled as he strode off to get the drive moving again through the pass.

At last the footsore cattle emerged from the mountain trail onto the old Cariboo wagon road. But danger still lurked ahead. This time it was the turgid waters of the Fraser River that threatened them. As it narrowed into the canyon it tore relentlessly at the rocky walls that confined it. At one point it had boiled over the cribbing and its swirling waters had flooded over the roadway.

The herd was halted. Three cowboys, men and horses roped together, moved slowly forward to test the depth and make certain the road had not been washed out. It was a dangerous job. The men let their wise little cayuses pick their way at their own speed and depended upon their instinct to stop them if they sensed the crumbling edge of a washout. If this instinct failed them, only the slender lariats

could save both horse and rider from a watery grave. But the
work of the Royal Engineers who had built the road had
been well done. The cribbing had withstood the strain and
the water proved to be quite shallow. Slowly the herd moved
forward again, strung out in a long line and hugging the
inside of the road.

The day came finally when the cavalcade rounded a curve
and came within sight of the mouth of the canyon. Beyond the next turn lay the town of Yale. Sam Moore
hurried ahead to warn the townspeople of their approach
and make arrangements for the immediate loading of his
cattle on the boat.

Bill Forsman rode in front when the herd finally poured
into the busy little town. Warned by Sam, the whole population, on hearing the echo of the approaching hooves, had
temporarily deserted the streets. Even the dogs had been
chased into the shelter of the buildings. But curious eyes
gazed from the windows as the file moved slowly forward
and turned down to where the coast-bound steamer lay at the
little wharf.

These were range cattle to which even a single man on
foot was cause for alarm. To them the town was full of
terrors. Nervously they began to bunch together and tossed
their long horns into the air. It took all the skill of their
herders to hold them steady.

As is the case with all herds of cattle, one huge steer had
assumed leadership of the drive from its start. Two of the
cowboys closed in and guided him towards the steamer.
The other animals followed him. If keeping the herd
together on the street was difficult, loading them was even
more so. The captain of the boat had already warned
all passengers to keep off the decks and remain out of sight
until the last beast was on board. With infinite patience

the cowboys edged the leader towards the ramp which led into the hold. The great beast stopped for a moment as he approached it and gazed wildly about him. The cowboys moved their ponies closer and forced him onto the gangway. Everything was going well.

Then it happened!

A door on the upper deck was flung open with a bang and a dishevelled figure lurched over to the rail. Gazing downwards his bleary eyes took in the scene below him. Before the startled cowboys could make a move, the celebrating passenger doffed his wide-brimmed hat and waved it in the air. Then shouting "Ride 'em, cowboy," he flung the hat down onto the horns of the animal below.

Bellowing with fear, the steer leaped towards the railing that held him on the ramp. The structure crashed into splinters under his weight. With a splash he hit the water below and scrambled for the shore. Tearing up the bank, his head down and his tail high in the air, he headed at full speed up the main street of the town.

Meantime many of the townspeople had left the shelter of the buildings and gone about their business. With screams of terror they now scattered before the mad stampede of the steer. But some of the dogs who had again invaded the street couldn't resist the invitation to the chase. One after another and in full cry they tore after the fugitive. As the receding din proclaimed the progress of the mad flight, doors opened, windows were flung up and the whole town watched the unwelcome visitor and his yapping pursuers disappear towards Hope in a cloud of dust.

Back at the wharf the cowboys managed to hold steady the rest of the herd.

But Sam, who had dismounted to superintend the loading, had for a moment lost his head and rushed after the

stampeding steer on foot. He was on the main street before
he realized what he was doing. He stopped and looked about
him. Nearby a saddle horse was tied in front of a building.
He untied it, leaped into the saddle, and lashing the startled
cayuse with the end of the reins, headed in the direction
of the cloud of dust which still swirled on the distant
horizon. As he tore along, he passed dog after dog, which,
having given up the chase, was ambling back to town.

Sam didn't know that the horse he had borrowed belonged
to the local butcher. This man had just ridden in from out
of town. The butcher knew that the town was in a state of
mad excitement but he had, as yet, had no time to find out
the cause. He turned as he entered his shop to see his
horse disappear, some rider on its back. The thought flashed
into his mind that a robbery had taken place and the bandit
was using his horse to escape.

Rushing out onto the street he saw a buckboard and team
of horses standing next door. In turn he rushed over and
jumped into this conveyance and urged the horses into a
gallop. The buckboard swayed crazily as he tore off after
the horse and rider. Some of the returning dogs helped him
to maintain full speed as they turned aside to bark at the
heels of the team.

What the outcome of all this might have been it is hard
to say had the frantic steer not taken a short-cut at a sharp
turn in the road. In so doing he ploughed into a soggy
marsh and sank in it to the point where his great body
rested on its surface. His race for safety was over.

Sam arrived in a matter of moments. He unfastened the
lariat that hung on the saddle and swung the noose over his
head.

His arm was arrested in midair as the thunder of galloping hooves reached his ears. At the same time he heard an irate voice shouting, "Stop, you blasted horse thief! . . . Stop!"

Sam lowered the rope and turned. As he did so the butcher drove up and leaped out of the buckboard even before it was quite at rest.

Instantly, his pursuer recognized his quarry. "Oh, it's you, Moore. I sure never guessed it was you. Thought some thief had stolen my horse."

In a few words Sam explained what had happened. As he finished a solution for his predicament flashed into his mind.

"Here's the biggest and best animal I brought down on this drive. What'll you give me for him as he stands?"

The butcher scratched his head. Then a shrewd glint came into his eyes as he looked at the trapped steer.

"Mighty big job getting him clear of that mud. Give you five dollars."

"Sold." Sam's acceptance was instantaneous. "He's all yours. I must get back and see what's happened to the rest of my herd. Guess I'll have to borrow your horse for the return trip."

"Sure, sure, that's fine. But I thought, with the fuss and all in town, I was chasin' a bad man."

The excitement was all over when Sam reached the town again. The cattle were aboard the steamer and she was ready to sail. Sam issued generous cheques to his foreman and the cowboys as rewards for a job well done. A blast of the steamer's whistle warned that the gangplank was being pulled in. He and three of the cowboys climbed on board. The latter would help with the unloading at Victoria where the cattle would be sold.

The four men stood at the rail as the mooring ropes were cast off and the boat moved out into the stream. From the wharf Forsman and the others waved goodbye and then turned to mount their horses. Sam watched as they rode towards the main street. Another drive was over. Both men and cattle had survived its dangers. He would get a good price for the animals in the hold. He smiled with satisfaction.

Yes, life in the Nicola Valley was a good one in spite of present hardships. Dreams of the future, when the coming of the railway would make life easier, possessed him as he turned and went inside.

The Stolen Church

A Story of Father Pat

This is the story of a most unusual theft. It was committed by three well-meaning people who refused to sit idly by and see what they considered an injustice done to their best friend.

When the Canadian Pacific Railway was building its line through the interior of British Columbia, the town of Donald was its mountain divisional headquarters. It was a typical frontier settlement which served for a time as the business and government centre of that part of the Kootenay country. The Reverend Henry Irwin, an Anglican missionary, was without doubt the most widely known and best-loved person in Donald. Few people, however, knew him by that name. To rough prospector, gambler, and railway worker he was affectionately known as Father Pat, a name well earned by his ready Irish wit and his genial nature. He could joke with a boisterous crowd or comfort the last hours and quiet the haunting fears of dying men who confessed to him the dark secrets which lay heavy on their souls.

It was a common sight to see Father Pat start out from

Donald on his errands of mercy, on horseback or afoot. He wore stout overalls, heavy turtle-neck sweater and hob-nailed shoes instead of the conventional clerical garb. But to the prospector or lumberjack lying sick and alone in a cabin in the hills, the good Father was a welcome sight in any garb. The burly figure inspired confidence and his twinkling blue eyes and cheery red-whiskered face smiled their message of hope. Putting down his well-worn knapsack with its load of food and medical supplies he would hasten to light a fire. Nor would he leave the sick man as long as he was needed.

It was indeed fitting that a fine church should be provided for Father Pat by his many friends in Donald. They built it complete with a six-hundred pound, silver-toned bell and a handsomely bound Bible. The latter arrived as a gift from the Theological College at Litchfield, England. The church was consecrated by the Bishop of the Diocese of New Westminster in 1889, and Donald became the envy of the people of Revelstoke and other communities in that almost churchless wilderness.

Among Father Pat's best friends and staunchest admirers were the widow O'Reilly and her friends the Copes. The good priest had helped to establish them in the town and their gratitude knew no bounds. Well did the widow know that the railway workers who filled her boarding-house had been sent to her by Father Pat, although he laughingly told her it was her own cooking that had attracted and held them. And equally well did the Copes realize that they would never have been able to set up and stock their store without his assistance.

But Donald's prosperity was short-lived. Unlike Rossland and Cranbrook, with their continuing and growing mining activities, Donald depended for its very life upon its position as divisional headquarters of the railway. But the company found it to its advantage to move its Kootenay headquarters to Revelstoke. This decision, which would convert Donald into little more than a ghost town, was made while Father Pat was away. He was holding special services in Golden. Mr. and Mrs. Cope decided to go to Windermere and start a new business there. The widow O'Reilly made up her mind to accompany them.

But before they could get away, a shocking piece of news reached Mrs. O'Reilly's ears. Father Pat's church was to be moved, just as it stood, to Revelstoke. To the good widow this was little less than sacrilege. "And to think that while the poor man is away, they steal his church!" she angrily exclaimed. But at the word *steal*, a glint came into her eyes.

All that day the widow O'Reilly was very absent-minded as she packed her belongings. But when evening came she hurried over to see Mr. and Mrs. Cope with an astounding suggestion. Mr. Cope's amazement and doubt soon gave way, however, to excited interest as he thought the matter over. He began to consider how the widow's plan might be put into effect. Both he and his wife agreed with her that it was their duty to save Father Pat's church for him. Mrs. O'Reilly felt confident that they could rely on the help of every man living in her boarding-house. By midnight they had mapped out a course of action.

Early next morning they took the widow's boarders into their confidence and received assurance of their wholehearted support. The railwaymen would do their part. Then Mrs. O'Reilly slipped into the church and removed the handsome Bible. She stored it among her personal effects.

A few nights later an engine was heard puffing up the track towards Donald. A number of flat cars rolled along behind it. As the train pulled into the station, dark figures jumped to the ground and hurried to the church where the

Copes and Mrs. O'Reilly waited. Work commenced at once. Great shrouded objects were carried to the flat cars, and when the work was finally finished, the cars rolled off into the night.

Mr. Cope was standing by the engineer as they reached Golden. There a barge was moored ready to receive the strange cargo. The barge was loaded quickly and silently, and immediately started up the river. Later its load was transferred to a waiting steamer.

Not long afterwards, when the people of Windermere walked by a well-chosen plot of ground, they saw a strange sight. There, complete in all its glory, stood Father Pat's church. It was Sunday morning and a few stragglers were sitting lazily on the porch of the hotel when the silver tones of the church bell rang out, calling them to service. Everyone rushed to the church. Father Pat stood on the steps, smiling and ready to receive them. Mrs. O'Reilly and the Copes were the last to arrive.

Father Pat explained to his congregation that he had been as amazed as anyone to find his church had been moved to Windermere. He gently reprimanded his three friends, hoping that they would atone for their sin. But his manner was not so stern as he wanted it to appear. The three culprits followed him into the church with the others, and it was a fine sermon they heard that morning.

For some time the whole countryside buzzed with horror, indignation, or amusement. This was indeed a new kind of theft!

Time passed and then, one Sunday morning, the bell in the steeple of the now famous church failed to ring out its summons to service. A little later it was discovered atop the church at Golden. Mrs. O'Reilly was shocked.

"To think anyone would steal *from* a church!" she exclaimed.

A demand was sent to Golden for the return of the bell, but the people of that town merely retorted something about people who live in glass houses. There was nothing to do but leave the bell where it was.

A demand from the Synod at New Westminster that the stolen church be returned to Donald received, if anything, less consideration than Windermere's request for the return of the bell. Indeed the good people of Windermere seemed suddenly to have lost their ability to read. Repeated letters received no replies.

Father Pat could never make his three unrepentant friends see the error of their ways. He continued his journeys among the scattered settlements where he was needed. With the passage of time the excitement faded and finally the church was reconsecrated in its new location. It became the centre of the social and religious life of Windermere. Yet it was more often referred to as the Stolen Church than as Father Pat's Church

The good Father did not end his days in the Kootenays. He died in Montreal while on his way to his old home in Ireland. His name still lives, however, in the many stories which were passed on from the lips of those who knew and loved him. His courage, self-sacrifice, and faith shone as a light during those boisterous days in the Kootenays. No wonder that his unselfish life inspired the poet's lines:

"Athwart the chasmed deeps
We tread our narrow pathway to the stars
Like children, comforted if we but know
That, in the dark somewhere, one great heart beats
Which understands—one partner who has blazed
A shining way across the Great Divide."

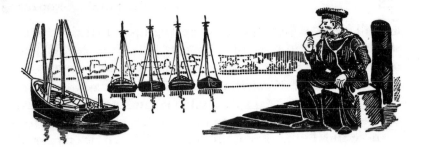

The Raider

A Story of Sealing Days in the Pacific

The old seaman sat on the wharf and, watching the boats riding at anchor in the inner harbour of Victoria, remarked, "It's not the same as it was in my day. You should have seen this harbour when the sealing fleets were in."

I realized my old friend was going to tell me one of his famous stories so waited patiently for him to begin. He was one of the few seamen left who had followed the seal herds of the Pacific to the hunting limits of Russian and Japanese waters.

"Did you ever hear of the *Rosita* and her notorious captain?" he asked.

"Indeed I have. Did you know him?"

"Just met him once, but that was enough. I can tell you a story about him you'll hardly believe. I got it from the only surviving member of his ill-famed crew."

"I'd love to hear it," I answered eagerly, then waited patiently while he filled and lighted his pipe.

"Victoria never saw better times than during the sealing days. Why, our sealing ships built this town; ships' chandlers and all kinds of business houses sprang up at that time. Our schooners came in here after hunting trips to be refitted and overhauled." His eyes twinkled as he went on.

'This dignified Victoria was as wild a port as you'd find anywhere in those days . . . saloons, and music halls . . . everything the lads wanted to squander their money on after a successful hunt. Even the Indians shared in the good times; we used them as hunters and their squaws were part of some crews, too. They were good at dressing furs and other work. You should have seen them after we paid them off . . . we'd drop them off at their villages but they'd soon be in town buying all sorts of gee-gaws." The old man chuckled. "A seaman got a good reception when he came home. The respectable women were just as eager for their menfolk to open a sea chest as were the other kind. They all got presents of Oriental silks, embroidered stuff and lots of things we picked up in the Orient for them."

"Did the *Rosita* come into Victoria very often?" I asked, to draw him back to his story.

"Just the one night I know of," he replied. "It was getting dark when a small schooner dropped anchor in the inner harbour. The paint was scaling from her sides and her worn sails were patched and re-patched. We knew she'd had many a long struggle against sea and storm. When the port officials boarded her next morning they met her captain and I guess they were suspicious of him. He was a tough-looking one all right; coarse black hair stuck out from under his battered cap, and hard eyes looked coldly from the scarred face which topped a powerful body. The officers demanded his ship's papers. These indicated that his vessel, the *Rosita*, of Mexican registry out of the port of Acapulco, had just returned from the sealing grounds off the Siberian coast.

"Looking at the hard faces and shifty eyes of the crew, the officers said later, they realized they were just such a gang of cut-throats as would serve under such a captain. They knew this so-called Captain Mareno had a bad reputation among the men of the Pacific sealing fleets.

"Mareno, as he called himself, said that he had run into Victoria to have his ship overhauled. The port officers told him that as soon as his papers were checked and found to be in order, his vessel would be cleared. Meantime, he and his crew were ordered to stay aboard.

"The authorities hastened to investigate Captain Mareno and his ship. Wires were sent to the Mexican port named in his ship's papers. The reply came back saying that no such ship and no master named Mareno appeared on their records. The officials hurried to the wharf to interview the imposter. They found the berth which the *Rosita* had occupied, empty. She had slipped her moorings and was again out on the high seas seeking new adventures."

"Where did she go to?"

"I didn't find out until I met the only member of her crew who lived after the shipwreck. He was a bad one all right and may have been boasting but here's what he told me."

"That night, when the *Rosita* slipped out of the harbour, she started for the sealing grounds off the coast of Japan. Storms swept her southward until she picked up the trade winds and soon her crew was searching the horizon for the migrating seal herds headed for the Aleutian Islands. Luck seemed to have deserted them, however, and although they worked their way northward again no seals were taken. Steering north-west, they approached Siberia and at last, on the edge of Russian waters, ran into the herds.

"Did they dare to invade these forbidden grounds? Could

they risk being picked up by a Russian patrol? The penalty was severe. Poaching vessels were confiscated and their crews sentenced to work in the salt mines. No patrol vessel had been sighted, however, and the weather was hazy. They might get away with a quick raid!

"A few days later, the schooner's hold bulging with their loot of seal skins, they met disaster. A patrol boat overhauled them. Cannon shots across their bows made them heave to. They were taken to a small station on the Siberian coast, their schooner was tied up, and the furs unloaded.

Mareno and his crew were bound hand and foot and thrown into a room with barred windows, a few hundred feet from where the garrison had its headquarters. Later, they would be taken to one of the larger ports for trial. Meantime, the boat which had captured them sailed away in search of other marauders. During the first night the captain managed to drag himself to where an iron stanchion supported one of the uprights in the little building. He used the edge of this to rub through the ropes which bound him.

Later, looking carefully through the single small window, he noticed that there was only one guard outside their prison, and that it was only a few hundred yards to the wharf where his schooner lay alongside a second small sealing vessel.

That night, when all was quiet, Mareno threw off his bonds and swiftly untied his men. Warning them to be quiet, he hurried to one of the crude bunks and wrenched off a stout board. With this as a lever he used his great strength to bend the bars on the window so that his smallest companion could squeeze through the opening. Once through, the man moved silently to where the sleepy guard stood on duty. A brief struggle in the dark, and the guard lay dead. The door was unbarred and the prisoners sprinted through the night to their schooner lying against the wharf.

There was only one watchman aboard the *Rosita* and they soon took care of him.

But they had to have arms and supplies if they were to make good their escape and continue their hunt for seals. Perhaps the schooner lying alongside the *Rosita* could supply these! It could and it did.

While Mareno and some of his men threw guns, ammunition, and supplies aboard their little tramp, others loosened hawsers and raised sails. Everyone was working like mad. They had all the guns they needed and had made a start on the food from the other ship when a light flashed through the darkness from the post ashore. Someone had heard them.

Shouts followed the clang of a bell and the guards raced for the wharf. But they were too late. Her sails billowing out in the night wind, a stretch of water separated the *Rosita* from the land. Shots poured vainly into the escaping schooner as she drew away. Mareno and his crew were free and his ship was under sail once more. True, two of her crew had been killed and three wounded and they had food for only a few days. But they had arms and ammunition and they were free. The important thing now was to get out of Russian waters. All sails were set and the *Rosita* raced through the night.

The scanty food supply was carefully rationed. They dared not stop to look for the seal herds which would have supplied food as well as pelts. A patrol might already be on their trail. Luck favoured them, however, the winds were off shore, and every mile meant greater safety. At last Mareno felt that they were well beyond the chance of capture. He altered his course time and again. He was once more on the prowl, but this time not for seals. Food was the imperative need. Also, he dared not make any Pacific port without furs with which to raise money. There was only one way to get what he needed.

Days passed as they scoured the sea for a victim. The sealing grounds offered none. Storms buffeted their vessel and dense fogs impeded their search. Their condition grew daily more and more desperate. Then, late one afternoon, they sighted a sail in the distance. Setting a course to overhaul it, they came close enough to see that it was flying the Japanese flag. This was indeed luck. It would be months before the loss of a Japanese sealer could be traced to the *Rosita* and her master. The chances were they would never be connected with its disappearance. There was one way to make sure of that!

As Mareno stood at the rail a light fog drifted about them, a fog, which the captain knew, would grow denser as night fell. Faint whistles reached his ears from the other craft, and Mareno smiled as he realized that the hunting boats were being called in. His victim would be forced to lie to during the night. He hailed the stranger and moved on as though heading westward. But as soon as the fog closed about them he ordered the *Rosita* to heave to.

After dark hunting boats were lowered from the *Rosita* and manned by well-armed ruffians. Only the cook and cabin boy were left on board with orders to start lighting flares to guide the boats back at a given signal. The boats prowled through the murk, keeping within hailing distance of each other. Mareno had spent his life on the water and his instinct for distances and direction was almost perfect.

In less than half an hour their victim loomed out of the fog. Silently, the hunters approached her lights. Mareno figured there would be only one watchman on deck. His boat slipped to the side of the Japanese schooner. Noiselessly a grappling iron was thrown over the rail and Mareno swarmed up the rope. He stole forward, taking shelter behind the deck-house. A movement in the bow caught his eye . . . the watchman. A minute later, powerful hands seized the unsuspecting Japanese from behind. Mareno called softly to his companions and they soon climbed aboard. The sleepy crew was already stirring, little knowing what was in store for them. It was all over for them in a matter of minutes.

The flares from the *Rosita* guided back the hunting boats. Later, she was moved alongside the prize and by noon next day, food arms and ammunition and best of all, a rich cargo of seal skins were transferred to her hold. The last act was to scuttle the captured sealer and watch her and her dead crew sink out of sight and, as the watchers hoped, out of the minds of men.

The *Rosita* turned and started on her voyage towards American waters. But she was delayed by calms, then harried by storms. It seemed as though fate was determined to hand her back into the hands of the port officials at Victoria, from whom she had escaped long months before.

During one lashing storm her captain, struggling desperately to save her, reluctantly ordered everything jettisoned that could be moved. Overboard went the coveted bales of seal skins and the arms and ammunition so mercilessly taken from her victims. But it was too late. The waterlogged *Rosita,* no longer able to respond to her helm, wallowed helplessly. She was not far from the coast of Vancouver Island when she met her fate. She sank in the graveyard of the Pacific. Her brigand crew with their captain joined their many victims. Only one man was found, clinging to a piece of wreckage. He was picked up and brought into Victoria." The old seaman finished speaking.

"What happened to him?" I asked.

"Finally drifted back to sea in another ship, I guess. The authorities didn't know his story so there was no charge against him. I met him in a tavern one night and he told me this tale." The old man sat back and, looking out at the water added, "No, the harbour is not what it was in my day."

The Birth of a City

First Days in Prince Rupert

The black bow of the old steamship *Tees* plunged with an awkward twist through the steel-grey waters of Queen Charlotte Sound. Her decks rose and fell at dizzy angles as she moved with the swells that rolled in from the open ocean.

Clinging to her deck-rail stood a boy, his eyes on the distant islands to which the vessel slowly made its way. He was going to join the surveyors who had recently started work at Prince Rupert. There on Kaien Island, the terminus of another transcontinental railway, the Grand Trunk Pacific, was to be established.

If this event lacked the feverish excitement of the gold rush which had first called the attention of the world to the northlands of Canada, yet the name, Prince Rupert, loomed large in the headlines of the time. The press told of its magnificent harbour five hundred miles north of Vancouver, but many hundreds of miles nearer the ports of the Orient. Articles described it as an ocean outlet to an unexploited empire of unlimited resources—fish, minerals, timber and land. According to them here was an Eldorado of a different kind from the Yukon but of even greater promise. Reading the glowing predictions regarding its future, people everywhere on the continent checked over their bank accounts and awaited the day when the city lots would be placed on the market.

Something of this dream possessed the boy as he gazed over the restless waters of the Sound. Tomorrow he would arrive at his destination to identify himself actively with the beginnings of a future metropolis, another step in the building of the great, new Canada. In a humble way, in his work, he would be one of the architects of the future of his country. His imagination pictured the city of his dreams. He saw its towering buildings, its busy wharves, its bright lights and its hurrying crowds of people. Impatience took possession of him as he glanced from the distant shoreline to the watch he pulled from his pocket.

He was a boy. His dreams were the dreams of a boy. Time cast no shadows over their glowing colours nor did a knowledge of economic realities threaten their realization.

The following morning the steamer nosed its way between Digby and Kaien Islands into the harbour of Prince Rupert. Heavily timbered shores marked the entrance and on the right hand rose into a high ridge, later to be named Mount Hayes, which formed the backbone of Kaien Island.

The steamer swung sharply to the left and followed an island-studded channel to the little Indian village of Metlakatla. Here is was that the zealous Father Duncan had laboured among his dusky charges until a quarrel with the church authorities led to his migration with some of his followers to a new site across the international boundary in Alaska. For the time being Metlakatla was the headquarters for the engineers employed by the railway company.

The boy hurried off the boat and soon met some of the men with whom he was to work. He learned that the mill owned by the B. C. Tie and Timber Company was already operating in the channel behind Kaien Island. A pile-driver had started work on a wharf at Prince Rupert. A street had been laid out along the waterfront and a main street surveyed and cleared which ran inland from the site of the wharf.

The next morning Columbia River boats headed across the harbour to the site of Prince Rupert. In one of them sat the boy, his eager eyes searching the landscape. He was still under the spell of his dream when, with the others, he stepped ashore on Kaien Island. But the building of a city is the task of long years. Here on this rocky island there were only the first, faint signs of man's encroachment. Here was primaeval terrain still wrapped in the silence of the north-land.

An hour later the shoreline echoed to the sound of the axes of the clearing gangs. This echoing chorus was led by the staccato notes of the pile-driver as it pounded home the foundations of the wharf. Already a toolshed had been erected, the first building of any kind on the site of the future city. Wooden floors for a row of tents along the waterfront were being prepared to house the growing crowds of workmen who were coming north on every boat. Man's conquest of another frontier had begun.

A shore traverse of the island had been completed and work on a topographic map was under way. The boy found himself allotted to one of the parties engaged in this work and, as accommodation became available on the townsite, everyone was moved across from Metlakatla.

In a few weeks the wharf, with its freight shed, was completed. A headquarters building with quarters for the head engineers and drafting rooms rose on a clearing nearby. And with the clearing and planking of the main street came Prince Rupert's first store, owned by Kelly, Carruthers & Company of Vancouver. A branch of the Canadian Bank of Commerce opened shortly afterwards and, as an evidence that civilization had indeed come to Kaien Island, a barber shop appeared across from the store.

Tents sprang up on all sides. Among these was one occupied by Moore, location engineer for the railway line on the island and up the reaches of the Skeena River. With him was his wife, the first white woman in Prince Rupert. She was a true pioneer. She enjoyed the rough life of camp and the welcome mat was always out at her humble home for the lonely bachelors on the island. Needless to say her hours were busy ones.

Winter on the Prairies suspended railway construction there and the resident engineers poured into Prince Rupert to carry on the topographic and hydrographic work which preceded the laying out of the townsite. Among them was Lincoln Ellsworth, later to become famous as an Antarctic explorer, and many others who in the years to come were known throughout the world for their engineering achievements.

They were a grand lot of men. The boy was proud and happy in his association with them and to work under their leadership. The other men who made up the rank and file of the survey parties were also an interesting lot. Some of them had gone into Dawson with the gold rush, others had drifted south from the mining camps of the Alaskan Panhandle, still others had been culled by employment agencies from the floating population of Vancouver's waterfront.

As the winter passed, permanent camps were built at strategic points on the shoreline of the island. From these the parties operated. Columbia River boats, in charge of Indian boatmen, carried them to and from their work.

The animal life on the island and the sea life in the harbour were a constant source of interest to the boy. As the weather grew colder timber wolves made the nights hideous with their howls and pursued their victims among the deer on the island past the very doors of the various camps. Hair seals, sea lions and porpoises played about in the chilly waters of the harbour and a large school of whales sought shelter there from the winter storms.

An incident occurred in which one of these whales played a leading role. The boy was spending the night at headquarters in Prince Rupert. He went down to the wharf to pick up something from the freight shed. It was one of the few clear, frosty nights that winter and a full moon lighted the waters of the harbour.

He was surprised to find a man standing near the end of the wharf, a rifle under his arm, his eyes gazing into the silvery reaches of the night. The boy recognized him as one of the engineers, an Italian who, as he had worked for some years in Turkey, had been nicknamed "The Terrible Turk." The boy called out to ask him what he was doing. A voice just above a whisper came from the motionless figure.

"Wheesht! Wheesht! I waita for da whale."

Under his breath the boy made his own comment and hurried into the freight shed. Some minutes later two rifle shots, followed by the sound of a great splash, broke the silence. Rushing out onto the wharf, the boy found the hunter hopping from one foot to the other in an excited dance. Over his head he waved his rifle as he shouted into the spaces of the night.

"I heet heem! I heet heem! He maka meet hees tail— once—twice."

Yes, whales were big game in any language. But a thirty-thirty bullet would do little damage to such a blubber-coated monster. No dead whale was found on the beach next morning. Probably, from a sanitary angle, this was just as well.

A number of Japanese axemen had been brought in and allotted to some of the survey parties. They were good workmen but the discovery of a supply of Chinese whiskey, Sam Suey as it was called, which could be had from a blind-pig at a nearby cannery, led to an incident that might have resulted in tragedy.

The party on which the boy was working was stationed at Camp Kelliher on one of the lake-like extensions that separated Kaien Island from the mainland. It was evident one evening that a supply of Sam Suey had been smuggled in by the Japanese axemen. Darkness had fallen on a snow-covered world as sounds of revelry echoed from the tent where the Orientals were at dinner. For some reason a quarrel arose between two of them. One decided to bring it to a conclusion by wielding a table fork as a dagger. His lunge just missed his opponent's eye.

Evidently this attack called for what to the Oriental mind would amount to a fair settlement of the dispute. The two antagonists were stripped of clothing and pushed out of the tent into the snow by their jabbering countrymen. A ring was formed with the two men in the centre and the fight was on.

Every man in the camp, attracted by the shouting, joined the audience. It was decided not to interfere. No holds were barred and no rules tempered the ferocity of the struggle. Evenly matched, the little yellow men fought on for over an hour. At last one sank unconscious to the ground. Swarming about the victor, his countrymen escorted him triumphantly to his quarters. They paid not the slightest attention to the still figure in the snow.

The white men, however, came to his rescue. He was carried into the engineers' quarters and his wounds dressed. As he returned to consciousness it was evident from his mutterings that his one thought was of revenge. The threat of murder smouldered in his eyes. The engineers decided to forestall the possibility of such a crime by sending him into Prince Rupert at daylight the following morning. He was not seriously injured, as was evidenced by the struggle he put up when he was bundled into a boat under a strong escort.

When enquiries were made as to the victor of the fight it was found that he had taken to the woods long before daylight. He knew that his adversary would never rest until the score had been finally settled. He was taking no chances on the tables being turned.

The busy weeks passed and the work of mapping the island neared completion. In the drafting offices blueprints of the first section of the townsite took final form and the forest on this part of the island receded before the attacks of the clearing gangs.

As signs of spring became evident on all sides, word arrived that work on the railway across the Prairies was to begin again. The engineers were to return to their residences. This meant many changes in the personnel and a complete reorganization of the work for those who would remain. A day was set for breaking camp. An air of excitement pervaded Camp Kelliher. The men there, irrespective of their jobs, had, with the easy camaraderie of the frontier, become friends. They had worked together and played together and had arrived at a common denominator of good fellowship. There was one exception. For the purposes of this story we will call him Percy.

Percy didn't know the meaning of good fellowship. He brought with him into the northern woods all the petty values of a confirmed snob. Everyone had tried his best to make him see the light and to get him to make some effort to remedy his shortcomings. Having failed they proceeded, in a good-natured way, to make life just a little bit miserable for him. They still hoped to see him change his ways.

In view of the order to break camp, it was resolved that Percy must be made the victim of one last prank. This prank must form a fitting crown for all those that had preceded it. It must really be something to remember.

No engineering problem was ever approached with more thought or planned more carefully. Everyone was in on it— except Percy. The day before the breaking of the camp, when the parties boarded the boats for their work, four men were left behind. Carefully they sawed out the floor under Percy's cot. This floor, as the tent was built on a side hill, stood about five feet above the ground. The sawn floor was then braced from beneath to stand any ordinary strain. Three of the legs on the cot were also sawn almost through. Last but not least a loaded shotgun was placed under the cot, its two barrels aimed at the one sound leg. This weapon was strapped into place and a line run from the triggers to the cot of one of the engineers.

Night had fallen when the parties returned and Percy failed to notice the preparations. After dinner, which his companions prolonged by drawing their victim into an argument, the inmates of the tent strolled homeward. Everything had to be packed and ready the next morning when the company launch was due to arrive and take in tow the loaded boats. This meant an early call and everyone, including Percy, turned in at once. All the others in camp were out silently awaiting the big moment.

As soon as his even breathing proclaimed to his companions that Percy was asleep, the cord was pulled. A roar from the gun echoed through the night followed by the sound of splintering wood as the screaming Percy crashed through the floor into the snow. The first coherent words from his writhing, pyjama-clad figure were:

"My Heavens! I'm shot! I'm shot!"

But, seeing the crowd watching him and hearing their roars of laughter, his terror turned to blind rage. Seizing a bit of the wreckage he struggled to his feet and rushed at his tormentors. Before he could do any damage he was seized from behind and dumped back into the snow. There he was held until his temper cooled and he promised to behave himself.

The boy felt a bit sorry for Percy. He couldn't help wondering if this rather pitiful person would always be the butt of the jokes of his fellow men wherever he went.

The resident engineers left for the Prairies and the work went on with a reduced staff.

At this late date a tangle developed regarding the title to Kaien Island. Time consuming proceedings and investigations held up the transfer to the Railway Company. Word reached the men on the island that the terminus might be moved to Kitimat.

Gloom settled over the scene at Prince Rupert and took possession of everyone on the island. Was all their work here to be wasted? The gloom deepened when one of the company officials committed suicide. It was rumored that he had induced his friends to invest everything they possessed either at the Coast itself or in the immediate hinterland to be tapped by the railway. He could not face the possibility of being responsible for their ruin. For him there seemed only one way out.

The boy's dream grew dim. He would go south again and

later if the legal tangle was straightened out he might return. So a few days later he again leaned over the rail of
the steamer *Tees*. This time a strange loneliness possessed
him.

He had been happy during the months on this island,
happy in his work and in the companionship of those with
whom he had worked. And always hidden in the depths
of his being had been the dream. Now he was leaving all
this behind.

As he gazed shoreward he recalled all the incidents of
which he had been a part. As he did so there came to him
the realization that from a wider point of view he was leaving nothing behind. He was taking with him, as part of
himself, everything that had happened. The sum of all
his experiences and the friendships he had made were bridges
to new and more worthwhile achievements.

That happiness which springs from a deeper understanding of life came to the boy. He watched the waves that swept
past him from the prow of the boat. For him she was
ploughing a furrow into the future.

The years passed. The boy never went back to Kaien
Island. The railway reached Prince Rupert and the sale of
the first lots held the attention of the continent for a brief
span. Afterwards, as headquarters for the halibut fleet, the
little city of Prince Rupert slumbered on through the passing seasons under its grey skies.

Then came the Second World War. A peaceful invasion
by thousands of American troops brought a sudden prosperity for its businessmen, work for hundreds of tradesmen
and excitement for all of its citizens. With the coming of
peace this wartime invasion was succeeded by an invasion of
industry. The future holds unlimited promise. Perhaps the
boy may live to see his dream come true after all.

The Outlaw Who Gave Himself Up

The Story of Simon Gun-a-noot

The story of Simon Gun-a-noot, who for over twelve years was the object of one of the most famous man-hunts in the history of Canada, is one of almost unbelievable endurance and ingenuity. His trial was an indication of the absolute fairness and impartiality of Canadian criminal courts.

This Babine Indian, tall and powerfully built, was a crack rifle shot, a capable hunter and a successful trapper. Good-natured and kindly in his own family circle and among his friends, he appeared proud and haughty to others. Those who knew him best were the least likely to take liberties with him, for, although he was never known to look for trouble, he was quick to resent insult and absolutely merciless when drawn into a fight.

Simon Gun-a-noot knew the hills, woods and valleys of the Skeena River district as he knew the palm of his hand. He had been of great assistance to the men who constructed the Government Telegraph line through that northern country. It was Simon's knowledge of the land which guided them in the location of many of the telegraph stations they established. The men engaged on the line knew him as a good guide, as did the big game hunters, ranchers and the prospectors who came to the Skeena district.

Simon's truest enjoyment came from his family. Like his father, he was intensely proud of his own people, and family honour was very real to him. Sarah his wife, was young and attractive, a good wife and mother, and happy in her home. When her husband was away hunting, or visiting his trap lines, she often took the children with her to pick berries. They also gathered rushes and bark for the skilfully-woven baskets which found a ready market among the white people of Hazelton. No man dared to speak to her of her good looks or her charm, for she was the wife of the powerful Gun-a-noot. None, that is, until two half-breeds came to work in the neighbourhood. Both were bold when drinking, but not so courageous when sober. Both felt the blood stir in their veins when they looked at Gun-a-noot's wife. They often met her on the path near the woods as she was on her way home with the children. Sarah dared not tell her father-in-law of their attentions. She knew his anger would be as fearful as her husband's. But the old man watched, though he said nothing.

Then one night Simon announced he was leaving the next morning on a long trip. He had been hired to pack supplies into Stewart. Sarah received his news in silence but a troubled look came into her dark eyes. Later, when her husband's parents arrived she busied herself with household tasks while the others talked. Her father-in-law glanced at her once or twice but made no remark when he heard of his son's long journey. The two men discussed their plans for extending their hunting grounds on Simon's return. His mother interrupted them to ask if Simon had a list of things he must bring back for his family. She chuckled as she added that she had a long list of presents for herself. It was not long before the little cabin was filled with merriment as Simon teased the two women about their "greedy interest" in his trip. His wife joined in the laughter and forgot the grim forebodings which had assailed her earlier in the evenlng.

Simon made good time on the trail and, a day earlier than he had expected, reached a stopping place near his home. This was the Two Mile House, a popular gathering place for the settlers of the district, where liquor was sold to whites and Indians alike. Simon decided to drop in here before going on home.

White and Indian friends crowded round him in hearty welcome. One man only stayed at the far end of the bar, one of the half-breeds who had frightened Sarah. Now, the man listened to the talk and laughter of the group gathered around Gun-a-noot and a jealous hatred took possession of him. He swaggered over to the group listening to the traveller's account of his successful trip, and asked insolently if he had been well paid for it. Simon realized that the man was drunk and trying to pick a quarrel, so answered briefly, then went on talking to his friends. But the other was not content. The half-breed shouted sly insinuations to which Gun-a-noot paid no attention but he decided to leave before the other forced a fight. As he reached the door the half-breed's voice rang out . . . there was dead silence as every man in the room heard his dreadful boast about Simon's wife. Everyone looked at the powerful Gun-a-noot, knowing full well how fiercely he would resent even the slightest aspersion on the honour of his family. Gun-a-noot walked slowly back into the room and stared into the slitted eyes of his tormentor. And then it happened. Not a man in the room was fully conscious that Simon had moved. He had

sprung at the half-breed in one smooth movement that caught the man off guard, and the next few minutes saw one of the grizzliest fights even that northern country had ever witnessed. It took half a dozen men to tear the outraged Indian from his opponent. Then, as they held his arms, he looked down at the half-breed lying unconscious on the floor, and, his eyes hard with hate, said coldly:

"Tell him, when he comes to, that I will kill him when next I see him."

When Gun-a-noot reached home he found his father and mother with his wife. He had no need to tell them that something had happened, but he greeted his wife gently when she rushed forward. He would talk with his father first, he decided, before he spoke to her about the cause of the fight. No one questioned him; they knew that when he was ready he would speak.

It was two days later when Simon's family learned that the half-breed had been found on the trail . . . shot to death. A short time later a relative burst into Sarah's home to tell her that the second man who had molested her had also been killed and the police were coming to arrest her husband.

Simon's father arrived first. He looked at his son for a long moment . . . much was left unsaid between them. Each knew the other's pride and what that pride might lead to. For Gun-a-noot to be hanged at the end of a white man's rope would bring shame forever upon the family. He must disappear. When he told his wife of the decision, she begged him to take his family with him, but he reminded her that he must be prepared to travel quickly from place to place. He would find a safe spot and would then send for them. Now they must hurry and prepare food and supplies for him to take with him.

When a police officer arrived from Hazelton he found

Simon's wife alone. She had nothing to tell him about her
husband's whereabouts, and he returned to report the disappearance. So the hunt started. It dragged on and men
were brought in from other parts of the country, men who
knew nothing of that northern land. Pinkerton men arrived
from the United States, but, as one old-timer said, they
threshed about in the woods so clumsily that even the wild
animals followed Gun-a-noot to get out of their way.

Simon's father was arrested but escaped from under the
watchful eye of the law. He scaled a fence, over ten feet
high, a feat his jailers had thought impossible for the frail
old man. He joined his son, and again some time later
the rest of the family eluded their watchers and followed
them. Simon and his father built a comfortable log cabin
in a remote spot.

There followed a year of danger and excitement for
Simon. His pursuers made it impossible for him to sell his
furs to provide much needed supplies for his family. In
spite of the risk, his father and he were forced to hunt and
fish. But loyal friends helped them by taking their furs
to the trading post with their own and bringing back needed
supplies. They avoided giving any clue to the police of
Simon's hiding place. One day a party of searchers dropped
in at the cabin of a Skeena Valley settler. He made them
welcome and as they were at supper a knock came to the
door. The settler opened it to find an Indian who told him
in a low voice that he was on his way to sell some furs at
Hazelton. He asked if he could come in and rest and warm
himself in front of the fire. The settler invited him in. It
was not long before one of the searchers started questioning
the native. But the Indian apparently could not understand
English. He soon got up to leave and when he went outside
the others followed him. As they examined the sled the

settler managed to get a good look at one of the bundles of furs. He caught the Indian's eye and turned to walk back to his cabin. The searching party saw nothing unusual in the furs and followed him. The Indian hurried off.

Later, when the others left, the old settler filled his pipe and sat smoking, deep in thought. He wondered about many things, particularly why an Indian who had thought he was right in vindicating his family honour, should be hunted like a wild animal; and why men who knew nothing of Simon or his country should be sent here to look for him. He chuckled as he thought that, if they had questioned him, he would have felt compelled to answer. He would have had to tell them what any man in that part of the country would have guessed at once, that those furs, particularly those fine marten skins, could come only from Gun-a-noot's traps. But they had asked no questions of him.

The years passed and the search went on. One day Simon was returning home when he heard voices ahead of him. Quickly he sought shelter and circled the men who were hunting him. As he watched them from cover, they sat down to rest and started talking about hunting. Simon smiled as he heard them agree that Gun-a-noot had been the only guide who could assure a hunting party big game. But his father looked serious when he told him of the encounter. He reminded Simon that he might become careless as time passed. His wife and children might some day be seen and recognized. They should move to the far north, the old man advised. But Simon shook his head. They were safe. Their little cabin was well hidden and they could see without being seen should anyone approach. But he told his wife to be more careful and keep the children close to her.

It was only a few days later when Simon's warning was proved necessary. His wife and children were in the woods

when one of the boys wandered away. He had flushed a
rabbit and was trying to keep up with it when he heard a
noise. He ran at once for cover as his father had taught him
to do. He saw three white men coming towards him, and
with them was an Indian whom he recognized as a friend of
his father. Then he heard another sound and, turning, froze
in horror. His mother had missed him and had started to
look for him. The strangers would see her in a moment.
Instantly he stepped out from cover and faced them. They
looked closely at him and asked their guide who he was. The
Indian shrugged his shoulders, then replied, "Boy, he just
look for berries," and led his companions off in the opposite
direction. The children and their mother hurried home.

When they arrived Simon was in earnest conversation
with a friend who had come expressly to make an important
suggestion. It was time, he said, that Simon gave himself
up. The search for him had lasted twelve long years and
the government had grown tired of the expense of sending
men into that northern country and keeping them there.
The government had already spent over $11,000 on the
search. Simon would get a fair trial if he surrendered.

Simon's wife looked at her husband in terror. He would
be taken to Vancouver, that big city in the south. His
people would not be there to help him. He would never
return to her. Simon saw all these fears in her eyes. He
thanked his friend and told him he would let him know his
decision later.

Again Simon and his father talked far into the night.
The old man was growing feeble and longed for the peace
and security of his old home. He wanted to see his son and
his family walk freely with heads held high, not skulking in
shame. But he knew, too, the chance his son would take if
he surrendered and was tried for murder according to the

white man's law. Finally, the old man sighed and spoke what was in his mind. They must go on as they were; it was the only thing to do.

But Simon did not have to abide long by his father's decision. Before the snow had left the ground that spring his father lay dying. Just before he passed on he called his son to him. They spoke of things that had been left unsaid up to that time. The old man told his son of a night when the half-breed and his friend arrived, drunk, at Simon's home. They knew he had left to pack supplies into Stewart and his wife was alone. Later, when her father-in-law had learned of it, he had wanted, like Simon, to kill them both. Simon clenched his fists as he listened to his father. He had never blamed his wife for his fight with the half-breed nor what had happened later, causing them all so much trouble and sorrow. He understood her desire to protect him by keeping silent. His passions had cooled with the years and he could now talk things over calmly and soberly.

Simon stood up as his father finished speaking. He knew now what he must do. He must give himself up and rely on the fairness and honesty of the white man's law. He told his father of his decision and turned and left him. The old man died a few days later.

Simon surrendered and the newspapers made much of this famous manhunt. Simon was promised a fair trial and he got one. Stuart Henderson, one of the best criminal lawyers in British Columbia, was assigned to defend him and, during the time before the trial, learned to like and respect his Indian client.

While Simon was awaiting trial in Oakalla Prison he had a visitor one day. It was the chief geographer from Victoria. He wanted Gun-a-noot to help him plot maps of the Babine country in the Skeena River district. Simon's dark, intelligent eyes shone with pride as he listened to this government official. He gladly agreed to help and, during those days of waiting, rendered invaluable assistance in mapping much of British Columbia's northland.

The day arrived at last when Simon Gun-a-noot stood before the judge and was acquitted. Free, he returned to his own people to move once more proudly among them after years as an outcast. He took up again his old life of hunting and trapping, and was much sought after by hunters who visted his Skeena homeland in search of big game. But no hunting companion was more welcome than Stuart Henderson, the lawyer who so skilfully secured his acquittal.

Simon took ill one day while out on his trap line. His sons carried him home where he died, surrounded by his wife and children. Gun-a-noot still lives in the stories told of him by the oldtimers of the Skeena Country.

Service First

(A Story of the Yukon Telegraph Line)

The Gold Rush of '98 brought to the attention of the Dominion Government the necessity for some means of rapid communication between the Yukon and the outside world. The only answer in those days was a telegraph service. The decision was made and one day in 1898 a construction party left Ottawa to build the Yukon telegraph line.

It took three years to complete this service, which has since stood as a tribute to the resourcefulness, enterprise and skill of the men who strung its wires through many hundreds of miles of virgin forest and rugged mountain country. The southern part of the line from Ashcroft to the Kispiox River north of Hazelton, followed the route of the Collins Overland Telegraph. This line had been started with the purpose of joining North America with Asia and Europe by way of a land line through British Columbia and Alaska. However, with the successful laying of the Atlantic cable, the project had been abandoned. The Indians found many uses for the miles of telegraph wire left stretching through the wilderness. At one point they wove its strands into a suspension bridge which was used for many years to cross the Bulkley River.

The parties constructing the new line worked from both north and south. At last, one day in September, 1901, they met at a point north of Hazelton on the Skeena River. The two wires were spliced and the task finished. In silence the rough, bearded men of the construction gangs looked up at the slim line stretched on the poles above them. Messages, in dots and dashes, would flash to and from the outside world. Settlement would follow now that direct communication was established. Another chapter had been written in the story of the conquest of the Canadian Northland.

Yet on that far-off September afternoon there was no celebration to mark the occasion. There was only a group of weary men who had cut their way through hundreds of miles of virgin forest to complete their task. They grinned as they shook hands, and for a few brief moments their cheers echoed through the hills. Then, once more the silence of the Northland took possession of its own as they gathered up their tools and moved off to their camps.

As the years passed the work of maintaining service on the telegraph line proved very difficult. Cabins were built at various points throughout its length. In each of these lived two men, a lineman and an operator. Each lineman kept his section of the line in repair and his duties kept him on the trail for long hours in all kinds of weather. The winter patrol was especially difficult. Snow-drifts laid their burden on the slim wires, breaking them down. Storms wrecked whole sections of the line. On mountain sectors snow-slides caused like damage. The lineman had to maintain a constant vigil. Meantime the operator, from his cabin, relayed the stream of messages passing over the line. It was a lonely life for the two men at each post. A visit from an Indian or prospector, especially during long winter months, was a welcome break in the monotony.

However, even this monotony would probably have been more welcome to the inmates of one of the cabins than a certain visit. The repercussions of this visit travelled many miles to invade the domain of officialdom and add, momentarily, a farcical note to the celebration of a unique occasion in a far-off city.

The wind was driving the snow ahead of it in angry swirls that Christmas Eve long ago. Harry Taylor, an operator, and John Torrance, a lineman, were sitting in their cabin in Northern British Columbia, finishing their evening meal. They were discussing the latest form of amusement which had originated through the ingenuity of one of the operators. It was a series of checker games. These were played in the evening when the line was quiet. The moves were relayed from cabin to cabin over the telegraph keys.

A championship series had been arranged, and now on Christmas Eve the final game was to be played. Harry Taylor and John Torrance at Five Fingers cabin had, as a team, won their way into the finals. As the game progressed, keys would be open in all cabins on the line and the lonely men would all listen eagerly. Perhaps they would forget their isolation and the Christmas celebrations of the outside world.

While the two men were talking over the coming game, the telegraph key on the table by the wall started tapping out Harry's call initials "FN." He jumped up and went over to the instrument. Another operator was calling from a distant cabin near an Indian reserve. He reported that one of the natives had failed to return from a visit to his trapline. A blizzard had blown up shortly after he started, and his people were afraid he had been injured or was lost. The operator asked Harry to tell his companion to be on the lookout for the missing man next day when he was on patrol. After getting the location of the trapline, Harry promised to pass on the message. They continued to talk on the key for some minutes and then conversation naturally turned to the final checker game. Asked if he felt nervous, Harry replied that he and John "had the game in the bag." He laughed when warned not to be too cocky about it.

Supper was over. Harry and John got out the checker board and sat down to a practice game. It had scarcely started when they heard a noise outside the door and their dogs began to bark. Opening the door, they were surprised to see an Indian, who stumbled forward and would have fallen if Harry had not caught him. Inside the cabin they found that, apart from hunger and exhaustion, there was nothing the matter with him. He had tried to find a short cut to his home when the blizzard overtook him and he lost his way. Fortunately for him he had stumbled onto the path leading to the telegraph cabin. A hasty meal was prepared for their guest. He was reported "safe" to the operator near his home, and soon he was curled up in a spare sleeping-bag near the stove.

A few minutes later the signal came through that the championship checker game was to start. The Indian was forgotten as his hosts sat down to their board and the telegraph key began to tick off instructions. Silence settled over the little room as the two players concentrated on their moves and the minutes slipped by as the game neared its climax. Harry and John smiled confidently as they studied a move. They felt sure it would corner their opponents and end the game in their favour. Little did they think that Fate in the guise of Indian Pete, their guest, would decide otherwise.

Pete had not gone to sleep. His dark eyes had been watching them from the moment they sat down, and he felt a great pity for these white men who were working so hard at a game that afforded so little amusement and certainly no excitement. A glow of friendliness and gratitude warmed his heart as he drew himself quietly out of the sleeping-bag. He stood up and silently crossed the floor. His eyes shone with excitement as he drew from his pocket the bag containing his gambling sticks. As he reached the players he opened the bag and spilled the sticks onto the checker board, smiling happily as he said, "We play real game, no?"

Too astounded to move, the white men sat and watched the carved pieces of bone scatter the checkers to the floor. Then a grim silence filled the cabin. The happy smile was wiped from the Indian's face and the puzzlement which followed gave place to fear as he watched the contorted faces of his hosts. Without speaking, Harry turned to the telegraph key and tapped out the words which told that he and John were out of the contest. Pete slowly backed away from John's cold stare as the latter said to Harry in a tone of ice, "I'll give our friend a start on the homeward trail at daylight. If he ever shows up here again, he'll be sorry he didn't stay lost." The visitor scurried into the sleeping-bag and lay still.

John was as good as his word. Dawn was just breaking as he hurried Pete out of the cabin. But just before Harry closed the door the Indian gave vent to his feelings. He had not wished to offend but to bring joy to his friends, he said. He was sad. Was there no way he could make up for what he had done? A present, perhaps? A big salmon? Perhaps some of his best furs? Anything they wished.

His offer was at first ignored. Then a smile came over John's face and he reminded Harry that New Year's Eve was just one week away; a New Year's Eve, he added, without any means of celebration, either solid or liquid. Pete had spoiled their only form of Christmas entertainment. Why not let him contribute to a New Year celebration?

A light of expectancy sparkled in Harry's eyes as he listened to the lineman. Pete would bring them a bottle of that excellent brew for which a certain prospector living near the reserve had a wide-spread reputation.

Pete was all smiles as he gave his promise—yes, he would return very soon. Then he asked eagerly,

"All good friends now?"

His good friends answered him that the friendship depended upon how he completed his errand. If he so much as touched the cork on the return trip, he had better take his squaw and move from that part of the country.

As he padded down the trail, Indian Pete congratulated himself on being once more in the good graces of his white friends. Their final warning faded from his mind in the light of this happy thought. When days passed and Pete did not return, however, Harry and John decided that he had forgotten about his errand. They thought no more about it. Something of greater importance engaged their attention.

At that time a start was being made on the survey of the boundary line between the Yukon Territory and Alaska. Correct astronomical time must be relayed by telegraph from the United States observatory at Washington, D.C., to Circle City, Alaska. This was to be made a ceremonial occasion. The general superintendent of the Canadian Government Telegraphs in Vancouver was invited by the American officials on the West Coast to join them in Seattle. On New

Year's Eve, Mr. Phelan, the general superintendent, went from Vancouver to "hear the time go by" in the company of his American colleagues.

Strict orders were issued to every telegraph operator in British Columbia and the Yukon to keep the lines clear for the fifteen minutes preceding and the fifteen minutes following the stroke of midnight. Arrangements were made to handle commercial telegrams in such a way as to allow this break in service. Nothing must interrupt this important ceremony. All details of the master plan were completed. This New Year's Eve would mark another milestone in the history of communication in America.

At the appointed time Mr. Phelan, as Canadian guest of honour, was seated in front of a telegraph key in a government office in Seattle. He was surrounded by a group of government and telegraph officials of the neighbouring countries. Expectantly they awaited the stroke of midnight. They listened as the Canadian manager at Ashcroft, British Columbia, lined up with Hazelton, Atlin, Whitehorse and Dawson. Dawson City brought in the American station at Boundary, and Boundary got through to Circle City on the United States military line. In the other direction Seattle got a clear line through to Washington, D.C. Silent attention masked excitement as finally, with mechanical precision, time signals ticked their way through from the banks of the Potomac to the far distant Yukon.

Mr. Phelan listened proudly. "His boys," as he called the members of his staff, were doing a good job. Every inch of line was in excellent condition; every operator was at his post and bringing through each time signal clear and distinct. Yes, it was a proud moment, and the Canadian superintendent beamed with satisfaction. The American staffs had also responded ably, and the officials in that room in Seattle relaxed in the knowledge of a job well done. Congratulations were heaped on the Canadian guest of honour, who graciously received and returned them. Everyone was well content.

But what was this? Smiles vanished and eyebrows were raised in astonishment as a strange message interrupted the flow of official congratulations. One of the Americans murmured something about the interruption coming from some station in northern British Columbia.

"Impossible!" declared Mr. Phelan hastily.

Everyone strained forward to listen. Faintly at first, then louder, came the urgent call "HN calling FN, HN calling FN." Again and again the call was repeated. Frowns gathered on the faces of the American officials as they recognized the source of the interruption. It was a Canadian station without doubt. This knowledge was conveyed in their glances directed towards their guest of honour. Mr. Phelan knew only too well the source of this transgression. The call signal HN belonged to the lonely station at Hootlinqua; FN was the call signal of a nearby station at Five Fingers.

Mr. Phelan turned to look at his companions whose frowns changed to looks of sympathy and understanding as they listened to the message tapping its way along the wires. It could be heard by everyone "listening in," all the way from Circle City to Washington.

In the meantime, Harry and John had played their part in the impressive ceremony. John had returned from patrolling the line, making sure that every inch was in good condition. Harry sat at the telegraph key listening intently. Both men had forgotten Indian Pete and his errand which was to have contributed to a pleasant New Year's Eve celebration. They shared the excitement and pride of the other men on the line who listened to the "time go by." They also

shared the happiness caused by the flood of official congratulations coming across the wires from all parts of the
continent.

Suddenly, in amazement, Harry heard the operator at
Hootlinqua break in with "HN calling FN." John heard it
and rushed across the room to stand by Harry's chair. Both
men listened intently to the words as they were tapped out:
"Indian Pete's been found on the trail by a trapper. You
will have to take him in on your dogsled. Better get to him
in a hurry; he's in serious condition." Aghast, Harry turned
and looked at his friend. John picked up cap and mackinaw
and rushed for the door.

Back in Seattle, Mr. Phelan recovered from the shock of
listening to the message that had broken into the ceremony.
He looked at his companions and met their sympathetic
glances. They had realized an accident had occurred and
that no time must be lost in rushing to the rescue of the
stricken Indian. As one American official put it, "Human
life comes before official duty." The others nodded in agree-
ment. Mr. Phelan again beamed with pride. "His boys"
would never let him down . . . unless . . .

Mr. Phelan learned the details of the case when he returned to his office in Vancouver. Perhaps it was as well he
did not learn them sooner and that his American friends
never did learn them.

True, Pete had been found lying on the trail. Also true
that he would have frozen to death in the snowstorm which
raged that night had he not been found in time. But when
John carried him into the cabin and dumped him onto his
bunk, Harry walked over and stared down at him. Once
again the two white men dared not move or speak until
they had their emotions under control. As John looked
down at the unconscious man, he muttered,

"Thought I'd bring him in as he was when I got to him. You can see for yourself."

Harry stared at the sprawling form and then at his friend. He nodded towards the object the Indian clasped tightly, even in sleep. John snorted in disgust as he looked at the happy smile on Indian Pete's face, and remarked,

"If I hadn't been afraid he was nearly frozen to death, I'd sure have konked him on the head with that bottle, that is if I could've got it away from him. Looks like his arms are frozen around it."

Harry nodded, then slowly said, "Looks like he not only disobeyed our orders not to touch that cork, but he darn near swallowed it to get at the contents of the bottle. That's what we get for trusting him with an errand like this."

"When he wakes up I'm taking him out and really losing him this time. He'll get us into serious trouble if he comes around here again. What do you suppose Mr. Phelan will say when he hears about this?" John's face was serious as he spoke.

But Mr. Phelan was not too harsh with his boys. He let them off with a warning to leave New Year's celebrations alone while on duty. They must set a good example to the Indians instead of putting temptation in their way.

Robbery Under Arms

The Story of Bill Miner

There was great excitement in Merritt that day in 1904 when word reached the cattlemen of the first train-robbery in British Columbia. Two ranchers from the nearby community of Aspen Grove stood in front of a poster in the crowded saloon and one of them read aloud.

"$5,000 REWARD will be paid for the capture of the men who robbed the Express and Mail cars of the Canadian Pacific Railway train near Mission Junction, British Columbia, on Saturday night, September 10th, 1904."

The words on the poster went on to give a description of the bandits.

"Say, this is serious," said Bill Haynes, as he finished reading aloud. "We never had this type of crime before. The railway company will be anxious about shipments of gold if there are going to be hold-ups."

"Well, hold-up or no hold-up we'd better get home," said Jack Sharp. "I have my stock to look after. Are you coming?"

Jack turned to leave and his friend followed him from

the room. They were riding along the trail when they saw smoke coming from the chimney of a log cabin. Bill reined in his horse.

"George Edwards is home. Shall we stop and ask about those horses he had for sale?"

"Guess we have time," replied Jack. "By the way, didn't he drive some cattle to Chilliwack? He must have come over the Hope Pass just after the hold-up. Remember, we heard that the bandits disappeared in the Pass, and the Indian trackers couldn't find any further traces of them."

"That's right. Say, perhaps George saw them." Jack was dismounting as Bill finished speaking.

The door opened as the two men reached it and a short, slim man greeted them, his white hair and his grizzled moustache in sharp contrast to his youthful eyes with the plainsman's wrinkles around them. Those eyes were keen and oddly penetrating. There was a suggestion of a steel will under the mild, reserved manner as he greeted his guests.

George Edwards was well liked by the ranchers and their families. He was generous and good natured to a fault. The children crowded around him when he visited their parents, begging him to tell them stories. He entertained them by the hour with tales of early days in the west when he was a prospector and cowpuncher.

He had arrived in the Aspen Grove district one day and after buying a small ranch settled quietly into the life of the community. He never spoke of his family, never talked about himself. He knew more than the average cattleman about horses and was fair in his dealings when he bought or sold them. He worked hard and left his ranch only to drive his cattle to market, or to slip off into the hills to work one of his mining claims. When his friends joked about his mysterious trips to these claims George shrugged and said he made a fair amount from them.

He was sometimes gone for weeks at a time and when he had been successful, he shared his good fortune with his friends. More than one unfortunate rancher had been helped through difficult times and his ranch saved by George's generosity. The women of the district all thought George "just the nicest, most respectable, most kindly old man imaginable," and often remarked that "he seemed much younger than his sixty-three years." He had endeared himself to them particularly the Sunday the travelling preacher failed to arrive and George read the service. Everyone enjoyed listening to his low, soft voice with its southern drawl. That voice was friendly now as he greeted his two guests. There was genuine regret in his manner when they refused his invitation to stay for supper.

"Have to get home, George," Bill said. "We wondered if you knew anything about the hold-up, or if you ran into the train-robbers on your way through the Pass."

"After I got back I heard about the hold-up all right, boys. But I saw nobody on my whole trip. It was pretty rough-going on the trail, as you know, and I had quite a time getting my animals through. On the road home I was pretty tired and would not have relished meeting anyone. Of course I didn't know the train had been held up, but I couldn't have done anything if I had run into the robbers." George's manner was mildly regretful as he added, "I hear the railway company is offering a big reward; mighty nice for some rancher if he could turn in those men." The conversation turned to horses and soon the two cattlemen left.

The excitement of the first hold-up had barely died away when the startling news of another and even more daring one reached the ranchers.

There was no moon shining on the sagebrush that night as the train twisted its way through the range land between Ducks and Furrer Creek. The train was beginning to slow down for the next stop, Kamloops. Suddenly, out of the inky darkness, two shadowy figures inched their way across the roof of the mail car as it swayed to the motion of the train. A third figure then climbed carefully over the tender and made his way to the cab of the engine. The engineer held the throttle in his thick-gloved hand and looked through the cab window into the night, unaware of what was about to happen. He whirled when he heard a voice behind him.

"Put up your hands . . . this is a hold-up! If you do what you're told you won't get hurt."

He stared down into a .45 automatic held firmly in the hand of a masked gunman. The fireman who was standing on the other side of him whispered, "Better do as we're told. This is Bill Miner."

The engineer gasped. The notorious Bill Miner, stage-coach and train-robber, was actually standing before him. He had heard many stories about him, the No. 1 bad man of the west; how he had held up stages and trains in nearly every part of the western United States and, when things got too hot for him there, had slipped across the border into British Columbia.

The engineer realized why Miner was holding up this train. The San Francisco earthquake had left a trail of disaster in its wake and Canadians were sending a relief fund to the destitute sufferers. $160,000 was the amount being shipped to San Francisco from the east. Miner must have learned of this and figured the money was on this train. The engineer knew it was not but he had no desire to let Miner guess this fact.

Bill Miner started immediately giving orders to the two masked men who had joined him. The bandits worked quickly and efficiently. They rounded up the rest of the train-crew and forced them to help in uncoupling the train from the express car singled out by their leader. Then the engineer and fireman were told to pull up the line a short way with it. The engine was again stopped and the order was given to open the door of the car and two of the masked men hurried inside. A short time later they appeared with only a small amount of registered mail.

Their leader asked: "Where is it?"

The trembling mail clerk managed to stutter, "The car is only carrying mail."

"You can all go now, that's all we need you for," said the leader after a further search.

The engineer and fireman hurriedly climbed back into their cab and as the engine started the engineer looked down and saw the masked leader staring up at him. The man gave a friendly wave and called out,

"Take care of yourselves . . . goodbye."

He turned and joined his companions who now stood beside three horses which had been hidden behind a huge rock. The masked men jumped on their mounts and disappeared into the darkness.

The engineer turned to the fireman as the train speeded towards Kamloops, "Was that really Miner?" he asked.

"It sure was. A friend of mine was on a train in Oregon when Miner and his gang held it up. He told me all about him and gave me a good description. Did you notice his voice and manner? Low, with a southern accent; I know now what my friend meant when he said he seems mild-mannered but you get the idea that he's a dangerous man

if you cross him. Still, he's never killed a man. He's proud
of that boast, they say."

"Tell me about him, Joe. I don't seem to have heard anything about his past. He seems to be quite a mystery man."

"Well," Joe hesitated, then continued, "Miner held up a
stage coach when he was only seventeen years old. He got
clean away with $75,000."

"Yes, but where did he come from?"

"He came from Kentucky where his folks had a good
farm. They were not rich but comfortably fixed. Young
Bill was a restless kid, wanted excitement and the farm life
bored him. He ran away and drifted to California. Those
were the days when the west was wild and lawless. There
was big talk of fortunes in gold to be had in California.
But young Miner did not find gold. He got in with an older,
hardened lot of men and decided to get his gold at the
point of a gun. He held up stage coaches and got away with
a lot of money before he was caught and put in jail. He was
in and out of jail many times before he was thirty-six. But
he never learned his lesson. He never smoked or drank. He
planned his robberies carefully, choosing men who were his
own kind. He is a cool customer."

"How did he get up here in Canada?"

"He found the United States too hot for him after a term
in San Quentin penitentiary," Joe replied. "Before that,
however, he disappeared from sight for a time. They say he
went to a small town and lived a respectable life. He took
a new name and even got engaged to the daughter of the
town's most respected citizen. But respectability made him
restless and he couldn't stick it. The night before the wedding he slipped out of town and no one heard of him again.
No one that is, except the Wells Fargo people. He held up

one of their stages and got away with a big haul. He was caught after a long search and sent to San Quentin."

"Wouldn't you think he'd be through with crime now that he is getting old?"

Joe didn't seem to notice the interruption but continued,

"When he got out of San Quentin he found things very different from the stage coach days. Trains had come into use. But this didn't stop Miner. In Oregon he held up the train that my friend was on. The railway company posted a big reward and the police were hot on his trail. That is why he slipped out of the States and over the border into British Columbia. I never thought I'd be on a train Miner held up. He is unusual all right. I can understand how he could live like a respectable citizen and no one would suspect him. It is because of that polite manner, no roughness about him."

"I wonder where he has been hiding out since the Oregon robbery? I wonder if he was in British Columbia all the time?"

"I think he was." Joe stopped talking to point to the lights in the distance. "Kamloops! Here's where the excitement starts when the railway company hears about what happened tonight." The engineer turned his attention to the throttle and the two men were silent as the train slowed down for the stop ahead.

The officials of the railway company were indeed upset when they heard of Miner's latest activity. They immediately asked the Mounted Police to send a detachment of men to help in the hunt for the robbers. The Mounted Police had no jurisdiction in British Columbia at that time but they sent a small detachment consisting of Commissioner Perry and six men. These joined the Provincial Police and the search was on. Time passed and still Miner could not be found. Rumours flew thick and fast in the Nicola Valley and the ranchers around Merritt heard all of them. One told of a constable going into a saloon at Ashcroft to look the crowd over and seeing a group of men at a table playing poker. The constable walked over to them and stood watching the game for a few minutes. Rumour claimed that one of the players was Bill Miner but neither the constable nor his fellow-players recognized him.

Bill and Jack laughed with the other ranchers over this story and Jack said, "It sounds as though Miner really is around here."

"Well, if he is he will be caught before long. Every man and even the Indian trackers are out looking for him. Why, even old George Edwards is away in the hills. Guess he's after the reward too. He'll find Miner if he's hiding in the hills." Bill's voice showed respect.

Riding towards their homes a short time later, the two friends met a party of horsemen who stopped them.

"You didn't run into anyone on the trail back there, did you?" asked the leader.

"If you mean Miner, no, we have no news for you." Jack's answer was short. The rider saluted and rode after his companions.

"Those were Mounties but they were not in uniform," Bill commented.

"Guess they don't want to be conspicuous, or perhaps they are not allowed to wear a uniform in our province," replied Bill.

The search ended suddenly one day when a Provincial Policeman following a clue sighted a thin spiral of smoke near a small stream. He crept quietly forward until he reached a thicket. Hiding behind it, he peered out and saw a small campfire with three men seated about it. They were eating their lunch and quite unaware of his presence. Quietly, he stole away; then hurried to find the Mounties. When he told what he had seen and described the men, the sergeant in charge made his plans.

In a short time the Mounties reached the thicket and took their appointed places. One of them walked casually towards the three men and began talking to them in a friendly manner. When he had made sure that his companions had circled the fire, he asked the three for their names.

Immediately one of them jumped up, shouting,

"It's a trap! Look over there! It's all up, we're caught."

He turned and raced for the nearby creek and the grove of trees beyond it. As he ran he pulled his gun and shot at the pursuing Mountie. He missed but halted to fire again, this time taking more careful aim. But before he could pull the trigger his pursuer fired and the bullet tore into his arm. His gun fell from his useless hand and he toppled backwards into the creek, making his capture an easy one.

Meantime, the other two had offered no resistance. The short, thin man stood silently watching the Mounties as they lifted the large canvas on which the lunch had been spread. Under it were guns and ammunition. The police took their prisoners to the nearest ranch where they asked the owner for a wagon and horses to take them to the jail in Kamloops.

The rancher, curious to see the notorious highwayman, Bill Miner, went outside. He stood and stared in amazement. George Edwards, friend of every rancher in the district, was standing quietly, his hands bound behind him. The rancher could not believe his eyes.

"What stupid mistake is this?" he shouted. "Why that is one of our most respected neighbors. That's not Bill Miner."

The Mounted Police told him of the identification mark,

a tattooed dancing girl which they had been told to look for on Bill Miner's body. It was there all right. But the rancher still protested hotly that many men might have that same mark tattooed on them.

The result was that the police had difficulty in persuading the rancher to lend them a wagon. Meantime a ranchhand went over to tell Jack and Bill what had happened. They rushed back with him to see what could be done. As they reached the ranch where the prisoners were still being held, Jack said to his friend,

"Don't think we'll embarrass old George by asking him what all this foolishness is about. But I do know what we can do, and we can get plenty of his friendsto help us."

In spite of all obstacles the Mounties finally got under way for Kamloops whipping the horses to a gallop as the old wagon swayed dizzily over the rutted road. Three of them rode close beside it. The other two sat beside the prisoners in the vehicle. The Indian driver did his best to make good time but the horses were not fresh and soon slowed their pace. The Mounties were nervous about the feeling which they had sensed in the ranchers. It was one of deep antagonism based on what they felt was a grave error. They had protested against the arrest of the man they knew as George Edwards, and had threatened to release him.

The wagon was lumbering along when horses' hooves were heard and a buckboard came tearing along from behind. It caught up to them and the two men in it hailed the policeman.

"I am Superintendent Hussey of the Provincial Police," one of them shouted. "Hand over your prisoners to me. You have made a mistake, got the wrong men. Go ahead with your search for Miner and find him next time."

The sergeant in charge of the detachment answered coldly,

"If you are Inspector Hussey, meet me at the Provincial jail in Kamloops and with my Commissioner's consent I'll do as you ask me."

He signalled to the driver and the wagon started up, while the Mounted Police crowded their horses closer to it, ready for action. The two men in the buckboard were silent, making no move as the prisoners were driven off.

"Did you see poor old George turn his face away when our plan failed," one of them said. "But he knows now his friends are still behind him and are trying to help him."

His companion watched the wagon disappear from sight then he nodded as he replied,

"Jack and Bill are going to be mighty sorry their plan fell through."

The final blow came to the ranchers when they heard what happend in the jail at Kamloops. The warden from San Quentin penitentiary arrived before the prisoners' trial. He stood and looked at the slim, quiet man who was brought into the room from his cell. The penetrating blue eyes did not waver as in his low voice with its southern accent he said, "We meet again, warden."

Yes, Bill Miner, who had lived respectably and honestly as George Edwards, the rancher, did not try now to hide his identity.

Jack and Bill were grievously shocked when this news reached them.

"He'll still be George Edwards to me," Bill said.

Jack nodded then remarked wonderingly: "How could he have gone wrong like that . . . him a train-robber! I still can't believe it."

Bill Miner was sixty-three years old when the New Westminster penitentiary gates clanged shut on him. He was given a life sentence but he escaped within a year. He was again the centre of a wide-spread search until it was discovered that he had slipped back into the United States. This discovery was made after he held up a train in Georgia and escaped with $60,000. He was caught and sent to Georgia State prison to serve a twenty-year sentence. He served only eight months when again he broke out and disappeared. Police, deputies, guards and bloodhounds failed to find him.

Mystery shrouds the final chapter in the life of this man whose iron nerve and daring made him the most notorious bandit of the west. He belongs to a past which lives only in the telling of it.

Flames Over the Kootenays

The Story of the Fernie Fire

"It is hard to understand how anyone can be careless with fire in a timbered country."

As he spoke Bill Downes reached for a match.

His two friends, Jack Sommers and Frank Goode were his guests this evening. From topic to topic their conversation had wandered until Frank mentioned a forest fire that had made the headlines that day. It had undoubtedly been started by a lighted cigarette tossed from a tourist's car. Frank leaned back in his chair as he replied, "Guess it's just plain thoughtlessness, Bill."

"Thoughtlessness, eh? Well, maybe that's it. But if these people had seen a prosperous town wiped off the map by a forest fire in a few hours as I did years ago, I don't think they could ever be guilty of starting another."

"What fire was that, Bill?" asked Jack.

"I'm thinking of the Fernie fire, back in 1908, I guess it was."

His two friends looked at each other. Bill had a reputation among his cronies for his stories of the old days, but it was not often he was in a reminiscent mood. Usually it was the events of the day that held his attention. Perhaps tonight a little prodding would get him started on this one.

"Didn't know you were in Fernie, Bill," Frank said.

"Yes, boys." Bill settled back in his chair, his eyes on the smoke curling upward from his pipe. "I was in nearly all the mining towns of those days."

"Fernie was quite a town, wasn't it?" asked Jack.

"It sure was. The population must have been around five or six thousand with maybe another thousand up at the mines, a few miles away. The town was wide open. Most of the bars had orchestras and none of them ever closed. Three shifts of bartenders looked after the customers and raked in the miners' hard-earned cash. What the bartenders missed was picked up by the games which ran day and night —mostly behind closed doors.

"But Fernie had many fine stores as well that made sizeable fortunes for their owners. Then there were the coke-ovens supplying the smelters and there was, at least, one big sawmill. Everyone seemed to have money and, as in most frontier towns, seemed to want to get rid of it as quickly as possible."

"How did the fire start, Bill?" Frank smiled at Jack as he asked the question, urging Bill on.

"Fernie is situated in a narrow trench, high mountains rising on each side of the narrow valley of the Elk River. A big fire had been burning out of control for several days in the timber beyond the little town of Hosmer. This lies a few miles north of Fernie. On the morning of Saturday, August 4th, another fire was seen to have started in the pass, southwards towards Elko. No one paid much attention to it although it seemed to be spreading rapidly and great clouds of smoke billowed from it into the sky. At the same time the fire to the northward seemed to be getting bigger.

"About noon that day the wind started to blow. It was filling the vacuum caused by the heated air from the Hosmer fire and as this fire spread, the wind attained almost hurricane velocity, sucking the fire to the southward with it through the pass. Unluckily the town of Fernie was in its path. By that night Fernie was a mass of glowing ruins, wiped off the map save for a handful of buildings."

"What about the people, Bill?" Jack asked.

"Luckily it was daylight or the death toll would have been terrible. Relief trains, running as long as they could run, evacuated as many of the women and children as possible. The Crow's Nest Pass Coal Company's office building which was made of stone and stood in the centre of a huge lawn, sheltered hundreds. Others sought refuge on sandbars in the river or fled northwards towards Hosmer. Even the company's coke-ovens were used as shelters. Fortunately, the deaths were few. A number of elderly people and invalids and one whole family which suffocated through taking shelter in their well, these were the only fatalities."

"Guess you must have had quite an experience yourself?" Frank was still waiting for the real story.

"Well, I did, and through my own foolishness, ran into a few terrifying moments. It seems you two want to hear all about it."

"We certainly do," replied Frank. "We wouldn't let you stop now if you wanted to."

"Well, as I said, it was Saturday and a good many of us stopped work at one o'clock. I had planned to get in some target practice on the rifle range which was about two miles north of the town. Some friends who worked in the Home Bank were coming with me. We all belonged to the

Kootenay Rifles. I ate a hurried lunch and changed into old clothes. I even dumped what money I had in my pockets on-to my dresser, grabbed my rifle and joined my companions.

"The wind was rising steadily and the air was heavy with smoke by the time we reached the range. We had fired no more than a round or two through the haze when we heard the clang of the fire-bell back in the town. This spelled trouble and we decided to call off the shooting.

"As we started back along the railway tracks the wind rose to hurricane violence and great clouds of smoke blotted out the sun. The air was filled with blazing bits of boards and shingles. Hundreds of panic-stricken people streamed past us, driven by blinding fear. They were going north-ward along the tracks. Some of them had snatched up what they could of their possessions and loaded them in wheel-barrows, toy wagons, in baby buggies or still carried them in their arms."

"Did you get back to town, Bill?" asked Frank.

"Yes," Bill replied, "we got back all right. We got rid of our bandoliers and rifles somewhere along the way. I guess we didn't take our soldiering too seriously. Anyway they did not seem much use in fighting fire.

"When we reached the main street it was a blazing in-ferno. The wind had torn the roof off the Opera House and it was lying ablaze across an intersection. Buildings crashed around us as the fire tore at their supporting walls. Firemen kept the streams of water going until the hoses became too hot to hold and began to melt in their hands. Yard after yard of hose lay where they had dropped it. Even the wooden sidewalks and the poles that supported the street lights were aflame.

"We reached the Home Bank building and for a few minutes helped to throw some of the books into the vault.

The iron doors slammed shut and our own safety then became our problem.

"I can't remember how we got to the river, but we did. The muddy water seemed a refuge so we plunged down the steep bank. Strangely enough, the brush along that bank wasn't burning. The flames roared through the town above us and over the house-covered flats on the other shore. Perhaps we could follow the river south and get behind the fire, or so we thought.

"Funny what ideas go through one's mind at a time like this. Some hens had found their way to the river bank. I made a mental note to come back this way if we needed food.

"We had not gone far when voices on the level bench above us reached our ears. So up we climbed. We could scarcely believe our eyes.

"Fires are unpredictable. A wooded park lay a few blocks to the south of the business section of the town. Clustered on its edge stood some of the town's best residences. By some freak, the fire had leaped over the park and some of the houses, to make its savage attack on the rest of the town. These untouched houses were what met our eyes as we hurried forward. The owners, with what help they could muster, were struggling to save their homes and belongings. Our help was welcomed. Shovels were thrust into our hands and we joined in the battle.

"The long hours passed unnoticed in our frantic efforts until at last the worst was over. We paused to size up the situation. A quick survey showed us that with watchfulness through the night, further danger might be averted.

"A few minutes later, one of the house-owners, a well-known lawyer, appeared at the back door of his house with a large rectangular box in his arms. Following him came one

of his neighbours with a huge tray of sandwiches. What could be in the wooden case? A few seconds later the pop of a cork gave us a clue. The lawyer had raided the bar of his club after the fire started. And so that night a weary, begrimed group of men were regaled on sandwiches washed down with champagne. It could only have happened in the Fernie of those days.

"As we feasted someone among us said:

"'Guess there must be something in that story of the curse placed on this town by the Indians. This is the third time Fernie has been wiped out by fire.'

"'Why the curse on this place?' someone else asked.

"'The story goes that one of the men who developed these mines was married to an Indian woman. Her people showed him the coal deposits. When he had profited by the find he deserted her for a white woman, so the chief of the tribe turned to his gods to avenge her.'

"'Just another of those stories, I guess,' someone said uneasily.

"'Possibly. But I've been in this town now for several years and I've yet to see an Indian stay here for more time than was necessary. In fact, I haven't seen more than a very few even passing through. Yet there are lots of them south of here on Tobacco Plains.'

"There was a restless movement among his listeners as their eyes gazed out into the night where red tongues of flame lit the mountain sides.

"At that moment someone arrived to tell us that there were hundreds of people spending the night on the sandspit in the river below the bridge on the Great Northern Railway just north of the town. None of them, including the children, had had anything to eat since morning. Had anyone any idea of how enough food for them could be found?

"My friends and I were young. Maybe the champagne had put us in a courageous mood. Anyway we volunteered to go along with the messenger of the distressed and see what could be done.

"The wind had fallen and the fire in the town was burning itself out. It was hard to credit the complete destruction it had left in its wake. Not a building remained save those few houses we had left, the coal company's offices and the warehouse of the Western Canada Wholesale Company. This last, like the coal company's offices, was constructed of stone. It seemed a logical place to look for food.

"We got the food all right . . . boxes of soda crackers and a whole huge Canadian cheese, coffee, condensed milk and sugar. We also managed to pick up a tin pail in which to make coffee and a number of small cans to serve as cups.

"We borrowed a couple of hand-trucks and loaded our booty onto them. The warehouse men waved farewell as we set off across the town to where the Great Northern station had stood.

We were lucky enough to run across a hand-propelled speeder where it had been hastily dumped off the tracks into the ditch. We had it back on the rails and loaded with the food supplies in a matter of seconds. Taking our places at the handlebars, we were off for the sandspit.

"Four long rows of box cars loaded with coke had been standing that morning on the side-tracks north of the station. Caught in the path of the fire, they ignited. The wooden cars had burned, spilling their smouldering contents onto the tracks . . . two great ridges of live coals. We hadn't the faintest idea of what lay ahead of us during the next few moments. We were gathering speed as we approached this airless inferno. Our luck held as the switches threw our speeder onto a track between the glowing piles of coke.

As the hot, acrid fumes struck us, we realized the danger. But we could not stop. Anyway, stopping spelled a choking death. We must go on. We drove the handles down with all our strength.

We gasped for breath, but hung on. Just as we emerged into the fresh air, the chap opposite me collapsed. But we were safe, the only memento of our brief ordeal, the singed cloth on the shoulders of our coats. I never knew before just how wonderful fresh air could be.

"Our comrade was soon on his feet again and on we went.

"It was a strange, begrimed lot of beings who welcomed us to their refuge. Most of them sprawled in groups on the sand, but many wandered about aimlessly. These were still in the grip of fear, worrying over their losses or separated from their families in the first mad rush for safety. We were able to assure the latter that their families were safe.

"It was good to see the effect our food and hot coffee had on those wretched people. We could sense the difference and soon the darkness hummed with the sound of voices and even an occasional burst of laughter added a note of cheer to the otherwise gloomy atmosphere.

"Too excited to sleep, I remember climbing up onto the bridge above the river.

"As I stood there the story of the Indian curse placed on Fernie by the chief to avenge the maiden deserted by her husband, came to my mind. Certainly the night seemed possessed by the powers of evil.

"Awakened at dawn from a fitful sleep, we decided to start back to the ruined town. Some of our many companions were stirring about. Probably a few of them had been able to sleep but most of them had just wearily stretched out on the sand.

"Climbing onto the railway tracks we found the flames

had burned our speeder during the night. So we decided to hike back along the tracks.

"The complete destruction of the town was even more evident by daylight. Smoke-begrimed figures wandered among the ruins, without aim or purpose.

"We found a haven in the home of the lawyer who had provided the champagne and sandwiches the night before. His wife and family had gone south on one of the relief trains, so we set up a bachelor establishment in his house. The one rule was that only those who managed to scrounge food of some kind could eat. That was when those stray hens I had seen down by the river came back to my mind. Armed with a revolver a friend and I went after them and bagged six within an hour. We returned with them and demanded breakfast on the strength of our loot.

"Meanwhile a relief train from Spokane arrived with food, tents, blankets and other supplies. Similar trains were on their way. Tents were erected and food dealt out to the hungry. Some of the doctors in the meantime had set up offices in the Coal Company's building and were giving free treatment for eyes damaged by the dense smoke, burns and other injuries. They were almost swamped by patients.

"Walking through the ruins, my friend and I heard the strains of a piano, expertly played and a chorus of cheerful voices. We found that a piano had been dragged from a house during the fire, into the centre of a vacant lot. There it stood the next morning, unharmed. Some of the towns-people could not resist the temptation it offered. They rigged up a seat from some half-burned boards and per-suaded a musician, who had been a leader of the orchestra in a bar-room, to play for them.

"The ruins soon echoed to such tunes as 'Too Much Mustard' and the 'Mississippi Rag.' A crowd gathered and one popular tune of the day followed another. The undaunted spirit of the Kootenays found vent in song.

"Someone joined the singing group to announce that a telegraph key had been set up in the park and free wires would be sent out to relations or friends across the continent.

"I left the cheeful crowd around the piano and on my way to the park composed a wire to send home. It told the whole story clearly in three words. It read, 'Safe but Broke'."

The Glow of Chinese Lanterns

A Story of the Chinese in British Columbia

One night at the turn of the century the Chinese people of Victoria were celebrating their New Year. The narrow board sidewalks were crowded with Orientals. They greeted each other gaily in their sing-song Cantonese dialect, and laughed excitedly as they tossed bunches of firecrackers into the air. Everyone held red-tipped "punks" and, as one bunch of firecrackers exploded noisily, another was lighted.

Some of these Chinese had arrived recently in Victoria to work as cooks or houseboys in wealthy Canadian families. Others were laundrymen. A few had been born in Canada, the children of Oriental pioneers who had worked on the construction of the Canadian Pacific Railway. Afterwards, they had washed the Fraser River sands for gold.

Ah Lee was a respected merchant and labour agent. Many of his less fortunate countrymen envied him. He owned a shop crowded with brassware, bamboo chairs and tables, fine silk goods, china bracelets in soft pinks, dull gold and jade jewellery. There was always an odd assortment in his window—sugar-canes, leechee nuts, Chinese ginger,

189

and herbs with strange Chinese lettering on the boxes, telling of the medicinal benefits to be derived from them.

On the evening of this New Year's celebration, Ah Lee stood in the doorway of his shop and watched and listened with deep pleasure. The dragon parade had just passed by and now the high, thin notes of Chinese music rose above the crackling roar of the fireworks. The Evil Spirits would indeed be banished for the year, he thought. This was the real purpose of the celebration and Ah Lee had done his duty by giving a handsome donation.

Suddenly he was aware of four people approaching along the crowded street. They were white men and the crowd respectfully moved aside to make room for them. They were the guests Ah Lee had been waiting to receive.

One of them was a detective and the others were men who did business with Ah Lee. He found coolies to work for these men, charging a commission which made it worth his while. He often paid the head-tax necessary before his countrymen could enter Canada, so, many of his countrymen owed him money.

He hurried forward now to greet his guests and take them through the store into his living quarters. Pride showed in his wide face as he stood silently watching them look about the room. He knew they would appreciate the beauty of the tapestries on the wall and the priceless jade figures on small teak tables. He knew also that his guests realized he was dressed as a man of his importance should be for such an occasion. His hands were tucked into the wide loose sleeves of his black silk jacket. His trousers were made of dark-figured silk and were gathered tightly below the calf. His shoes were soft corded silk with cork soles. He wore a skull-cap from beneath which hung his long "cue" braided with silk ribbon.

Waiting patiently until his guests turned their attention to him, Ah Lee's thoughts wandered to the one great disappointment of his life. He had no sons to honour him and his ancestors. Yet he would not go to China and marry until he could afford a wife of higher rank than a peasant. He had been saving his money and would soon have enough to pay for the daughter of one of the most honoured men in his far-off Cantonese village. His sons must be worthy of his position in this new land. He was brought back to the present by his friend, the detective.

"You are very comfortable here, Ah Lee," said the policeman, "but it's a shame that you live alone. Our laws should allow more of your women into this country."

"We're not as hard on you people as the Americans are," broke in one of the other guests. "They make it difficult for even you men to enter their country."

"That is true," said Ah Lee, "and my countrymen feel bitter about it. Many wish to live in the States where they believe money is found on the streets."

"Never get mixed up in that racket, Ah Lee," warned the detective, looking keenly at his host. "Smuggling Chinese across the border will get you into trouble; it may get you deported. We're trying to put a stop to it. Both the American authorities and our own are working hard on it."

At that moment a young Chinese boy, one of Ah Lee's numerous cousins, entered carrying a brass tray which held fragile bowls of green tea. He placed it on the long table in the centre of the room. The table already groaned under the weight of Oriental delicacies and sam-su-e, Chinese brandy, and other liquors.

In spite of the noise which drifted into the room from the street, the conversation was relaxed and pleasant as the men ate and drank. When the time came to leave each guest was presented with a gift, a small jade Buddha figurine. Ah Lee's grin was wide and happy as he escorted his guests to the door.

He had his hand on the knob when the door opened suddenly and a white man entered. He was tall, distinguished looking, wore a Van Dyke beard, and was immaculately groomed. He bowed as he held the door open for the others to pass through, smiling familiarly at the detective who ignored him.

Ah Lee was amazed when his uninvited guest walked past him into his living room but his face was impassive. Oriental hospitality required him to remain silent.

"I have come to wish you luck and happiness for the New Year," said the stranger. "I have heard a great deal about you since I arrived in Victoria, and I want to make you a proposition. I'll tell you quickly what I want and I'll make it well worth your while to do it for me."

The next few minutes were like a dream to Ah Lee. Following the warning from his friend about smuggling Chinese across the border, here was this stranger offering him an unheard of sum to engage in this unlawful traffic. Ignoring his host's protests, the stranger smoothly outlined his plan. He said he had a boat and crew waiting to take a load of Chinese across the border. He wanted Ah Lee to join him in the deal and his job would be to round up the prospective passengers.

Politely, but firmly, Ah Lee refused, then rose and stood waiting quietly for his visitor to leave. The latter stopped at the door long enough to slip a piece of paper into his host's hand.

The paper gave the number of a room in one of Victoria's cheaper hotels. Ah Lee turned it over; the writing on the other side was in Chinese. He read, and his face was serious when he finished reading. The stranger's plan was clever and held little risk for Ah Lee. All that night Ah Lee fought against the tempter and, in the end, gave way. He told himself he would only be giving his countrymen what they wanted most, a chance to get into the United States. Also, he would quit when he had made enough to fulfil his ambition for a high-caste wife and sons.

Early next morning he hurried to the hotel and was soon talking with his new partner. Later, as he left, he looked nervously over his shoulder. He thought he saw his detective friend but was not sure. He felt uncomfortable when he thought of him.

Everything was arranged and the night arrived for the venture. Even the dark, stormy weather seemed to be co-operating with them. Ah Lee shivered as he neared the dock where he was to meet the white man. For days he had worked hard and now a crowd of his countrymen were waiting for him in the shadows of the wharf. But his white partner was no longer genial and suave as he turned to greet Ah Lee. His manner was cold and hard as he asked:

"Everything in order? Are those your coolies over there?"

The other nodded as he walked to the group in the shadows. He spoke in Cantonese for a few minutes. His orders were clearly understood. Each man nodded then held out a bundle of money to their agent in this deal. The white man then took charge and motioned them to follow him. He led them to a small schooner tied up to the dock. The captain called to him and he climbed aboard. They talked for a few minutes then he came back down the gang-way to the dock. The next few minutes were busy ones as he herded the Chinamen on board.

The White man stood watching as the boat headed out of Victoria harbour and started on a course into the Straits of Juan de Fuca. The good people of Victoria were as unaware of their departure as were the Americans of their prospective arrival in their country.

Ah Lee did not wait for the schooner to leave before he rushed off through the rain and wind to his shop. He did not want to talk to his partner-in-crime and he securely locked the door. He sat in the darkness of his room behind the store for some time and his thoughts were not happy ones. Already his conscience bothered him. Finally he rose and gloomily prepared for bed.

Meantime, his victims were shivering with excitement and terror as the boat pitched and tossed its way through the dark night. They were chattering in their native tongue when the captain at last entered the hold and motioned for them to follow him. When they reached the deck he pointed to lights in the distance, flashing through the rain.

He and the mate hustled their passengers into small boats which were lowered when the vessel stopped. Eager yellow hands grabbed the oars and the boats headed towards those lights. The captain watched them out of sight then turned to his mate.

"I wonder what those poor devils will do when they find out that we've landed them just beyond Esquimalt Lagoon instead of in the United States. I'd hate to be that Chinese agent when they walk back to Victoria. I wonder how long it'll be before they find out we only ran 'em around outside the harbour . . . they're a long way from American waters."

"I didn't like that chap who made the deal with us," said the mate. "He's slippery as an eel and knows very well the real risk is ours. If we're caught the law can take our boat as well as send us to jail. Another thing, these Chinese we're tricking this way are going to lay for us some dark night when we're in Victoria. Did you get this guy's name?"

The captain shook his head. "I met him in a saloon. He's called the 'Doc.' That's all I know about him, except he's lived in China. He has a rotten name for games like this. Guess we'll get away with it this time but I'll not make another trip for him, that's certain. He paid me before we left. I made sure of that . . . but even big money isn't worth having a Chink's knife stuck in our backs or having them sink our boat, once they're onto this game."

"You're right. They're mighty vindictive when you give them a crooked deal and I can't say I'd blame them in this case."

Ah Lee lay awake all through that night with much the same doubts and fears. By morning, he too had decided that the "Doc's" scheme was not worth the price.

He was taking the shutters off his store window when a voice startled him. It was his friend the detective but this time the blue eyes staring into his were not friendly.

"I would not have believed it of you, Ah Lee. I always said you were one Chink I could trust."

Ah Lee's hands trembled as he laid the shutter on the ground. Never in their long years of friendship had this man called him by that contemptuous name, "Chink." He knew what scorn the other now felt for him.

"We've just taken your partner in this deal to the boat. We'd been watching the 'Doc', as he calls himself, for a long time. But when we caught him I never thought you'd be tied up with him. I'm sorry to say we have no legal case against him . . . but he'll never come back here again. The poor devils he tricked came to us with an interpreter and told us your part in the deal. I want to ask one question

. . . was the money you got worth losing the respect a life-time of honesty has won for you?"

Ah Lee was silent as he put his hand in his pocket and pulled out a roll of bills which he thrust into the detective's hand.

"Please take this," he said. "Give it back to those who were cheated. Tell them I did not know they were to be cheated but thought the bargain would be kept and they would reach the United States. Tell them I am sorry . . ."

His companion looked down at the money then at Ah Lee. He reached over and patted his shoulder.

"You're not bad and you're not dishonest. My guess is you had some good reason for wanting that money. I'll come down to see you on my next night off and we'll talk over what's bothering you."

Ah Lee watched him as he walked away, then turned and looked at his shop. He had nearly lost it; more important, he had nearly lost his good friend. His ancestors would not feel honoured if the money which provided for his future sons was dishonest money.

He went into his store and through it into his living quarters. He sat down in his high-backed, teak chair and staring at the brass figure of Buddha with incense burning before it, he thought of his ancestors.

One of his forefathers had been with the group of Chinese artisans brought to British Columbia in 1788 by Captain Meares. They were the first Chinese to live here and they built, at Nootka, the first sailing ship launched on this coast. Since then, his father's family had been represented here among prospectors, settlers, railway construction workers and farmers. They had worked hard and given much to their new country. Ah Lee stirred in his chair as he thought of how close he had come to dishonouring his forefathers.

He would go back to China with the money he had and find
a wife. His sons would come to this city and grow up with it;
they would do their duty towards this new country, Canada,
to which he and they belonged.

"It will be good to celebrate other Chinese New Years
in Victoria," he thought later as he lay down on his hard
pallet-bed and closed his eyes, once more an honest man.

The Invasion That Failed

The Story of the "Komagata Maru"

In the days before the dark clouds of World War I broke over the world, the citizens of Vancouver had a serious problem on their hands. They felt, as did most of the people in British Columbia at that time, that far too many Asiatics were coming into the Province. The population was small and if measures were not taken to prevent it, heavy immigration from across the Pacific would mean that the whites might some day be out-numbered.

Vancouver citizens staged protest riots in 1886 and again in 1907. These brought the intensity of their feelings to the attention of the Dominion Government. As a result, certain Orders in Council were passed which tightened up the immigration laws. East Indians were in a somewhat different class from the Chinese and Japanese because they were, after all, British subjects. But Vancouverites felt just the same about too many of them coming to their city. An Order in Council was passed which said that "immigrants entering Canada must arrive here by continuous journey and on through tickets from the country of their birth or citizenship." This included East Indians.

So, when word reached Vancouver one day in May, 1914, that a Japanese vessel, the *Komagata Maru,* was heading for Vancouver harbour with three hundred and seventy-six East Indians aboard, Vancouver citizens were alarmed. When it was learned that they had not come direct from India but had been picked up at Chinese and Japanese ports, Vancouver was indignant. This was in direct violation of the immigration law. These people must not be allowed to land.

The would-be immigrants had been promised by the man who chartered the *Komagata Maru* that they would be allowed to enter Canada and naturally they expected to do so. Many of their friends and relatives already living in Vancouver were waiting for their arrival.

Vancouver's waterfront was a centre of intense excitement that day as the *Komagata Maru* anchored well out in the harbour. Patrol boats circled the ship, proof of the immigration officials' determination that no one should leave it. On shore, every nearby office window and the roofs of the waterfront sheds were crowded with people who watched and waited to see what would happen . The tread of military boots echoed on the wooden boards of the wharf as militia units patrolled the area. The sullen, disappointed passengers on the ship realized how vain were their hopes of landing on these shores. The question on the lip of every watcher was, "Will they be allowed to land, or will they be sent back where they came from?"

This was soon answered. It was a clear night and the sea-going tug, *Sea Lion,* was lying by her wharf when special immigration officials and a heavy police force of 120 men under Chief McLennan boarded her. All eyes watched as the tug swung away and headed for the *Komagata Maru*. On her decks the East Indians crowded to the rail to await the tug's arrival. They were in an ugly mood. Deluded by their leaders, disappointed and desperate, they had staged a successful riot and taken possession of the vessel, refusing the Japanese captain and crew access to the engine room. Now they stood, lining the rail of the ship as the tug approached. They stared in sullen rage as the searchlight from the *Sea Lion* picked them out. The tug drew alongside, its decks some fifteen feet below that of the big ship.

There was a moment's pause. Then a deluge of missiles poured down on the crowded deck of the *Sea Lion*. Its passengers were helpless as huge chunks of coal, clinkers from the ship's furnace, scrap iron and heavy, garbage-filled crates smashed down on them. Clubs made from harbour driftwood and spears made by lashing knives to long bamboo poles threatened any attempt at boarding.

Chief McLennan was among the many injured. The tug's deck was a shambles and amidst the confusion those who escaped injury awaited the order to use their rifles. But it did not come. The Chief could not give it. It was not his duty to increase the grievances of these would-be immigrants by shooting them. So the defeated tug turned and made for the wharf. Triumphant shouts echoed across the water from the East Indians who were flushed with victory.

Feeling in Vancouver now rose to a furious pitch. Action was demanded of the government and the citizens wanted to know more about the purpose of the *Komagata Maru*'s coming to their harbour. Many felt that some sinister intrigue was behind this move. Credence was given to this when the man who had brought the would-be immigrants to British Columbia was quoted as saying that, if he did not succeed in getting his passengers into Canada, at least he would have the satisfaction of embarrasing the British in India. There were threats of war with Germany and the alarm increased when it was discovered that this man had chartered the *Komagata Maru* through a German shipping agent. "Was this a German plot to spread dissension?" asked one Vancouverite of another.

By this time the East Indians in the city were becoming inflamed by what they considered the unjust treatment of their countrymen. Some of them decided to smuggle arms to their friends aboard the ship. Slipping down to the State of Washington, they bought guns and ammunition. But our authorities learned of this plot and the smugglers were arrested when they crossed the border into Canada. When this became known, a demand was made that the government take immediate action.

This state of hysteria was relieved by what followed. Canada had, a few years before, acquired two cruisers, the beginning of the Canadian navy. One of these was the *Rainbow,* at that time lying in Esquimalt harbour waiting to be commissioned. Manned by a volunteer crew, she steamed under special orders, into Burrard Inlet and anchored close to the *Komagata Maru.* Her guns were uncovered, two gangways were ready for boarding the Japanese ship. Water hose was uncoiled for use. She looked formidable indeed to the startled insurgents.

All that day an armed police launch circled the ship. Towards evening the tension broke. Representatives of the man who had chartered the *Komagata Maru* and of its passengers, sent out word that they were ready to accept the Dominion Government's offer. This was an immediate inquiry into any claims they might have with respect to the ship's cargo; "conditional on the passengers now on the *Komagata Maru* adopting a peaceable attitude, refraining from violence and conforming to the law by giving to the captain control of his ship immediately, and agreeing peacefully to return to the port whence they came."

On the morning of July 22 the *Komagata Maru* left her anchorage in Burrard Inlet and sailed for the Asiastic ports from which she had brought her unexpected and unwanted passengers.

The people of Vancouver were relieved and satisfied. This was especially the case when the mystery was cleared up about the man who had brought the troublesome vessel to their harbour. He was a Sikh businessman. He had been running a successful business in Singapore and the Malay States when he hit upon this idea for adding to his achievements. He knew that those East Indians who already lived in British Columbia had written glowing accounts to their countrymen in India about this "land of promise." Many were eager to join them. So he decided to start a shipping line, bring in immigrants, then fill the empty ships with lumber for the return journey. But he had to land his passengers so he decided to make a test with the trip of the *Komagata Maru*. If successful, he would soon have a prosperous steamship line. If not, he would at least embarrass British rule in India which he bitterly detested and opposed. He had gone to a German shipping agent with his plans and had chartered the Japanese vessel through him.

But bloodshed and misery followed the ill-fated venture to the end. The citizens of Vancouver had barely settled down to forget the whole affair when the climax came. An immigration inspector was shot to death in a corridor of the Vancouver Court House. As the vendetta continued, three Hindus who had been employed by the Immigration Department were marked for death. One was found on the street with his head almost severed from his body. Another was shot dead. The third himself opened fire in the Vancouver Sikh Temple killing three of his countrymen and wounding six others. Some years later in India, his body was found hacked to pieces.

Trouble also dogged the would-be immigrants. When their ship reached Yokohama word was received that no one would be permitted to disembark at Hong Kong. They went on to Kobe and then to Singapore. Here again no one was allowed to land, for World War I had broken out and it was considered wiser that they should be compelled to return to the district in India from which they had originally come. Some of them obviously had obtained arms in Kobe, for on their arrival in Calcutta they staged a riot which cost the lives of some twenty-six people, including a superintendent of the Calcutta police. Of some two hundred *Komagata Maru* passengers still left on board during this fighting many escaped to cause trouble in various parts of India.

What connection the drama of the *Komagata Maru* may have had with pre-World War I intrigue will perhaps never be established. Certain it is that the ship was chartered for its Canadian venture through a German shipping agent. And, certain it is, that the crew which so quickly and opportunely readied the *Rainbow* to play her part in the incident remained on board to serve in the defence of Canada when war broke out two weeks later.

The Call of Silent Places

The Story of a Remittance Man

Trees crackled and snow drifted down on the backs of the sled-dogs as they padded over the white trail. The lead-dog, a large husky, stopped at his master's command and Barney Malone called back to his companion: "I'm ready to eat, what about you?"

"Suits me fine," Charles Stewart replied, hurrying forward. "Looks like we might find a dry place for a fire over there. Shall we try?"

Barney nodded and started for the nearby grove of trees. The two men barely spoke until their light meal was finished and they were rolling their cigarettes. Then Charlie asked, "How long have you been running the mail sleds?"

"About three years," Barney replied. "I worked in Hazelton when I first came north. When I decided I was going to stay up here I hit out for the Buckley Valley and homesteaded. I didn't make out very well so was glad to get this job packing in mail and supplies from Hazelton. What brought you up here?"

"I wondered when you'd ask me something about myself.

205

All these days that we've been travelling together, you've never once asked a personal question. That could never happen in any city in the south."

"Guess we make quick judgments up here; we try to guess right about a man when we meet him then let him tell us what he wants known about himself." Barney smiled as he added: "Ever been north before?"

"Yes," replied Charlie, "but only in Alaska. I'm a mining engineer with an eastern company. They sent me up here to look into some of their claims. By the way, you know this country well, you might give me some information about it."

"I can't help you much but I know a man who can. His name is Morrison, and he knows this country better than anyone I know of . . . lived here a mighty long time." Barney paused. "Ever hear of a remittance man?"

"Yes, there used to be plenty of them on the prairies when I lived there." Charlie's voice held contempt.

"Morrison was one of them, but he proved something. He proved there are good remittance men as well as bad ones, but we hear more about the bad ones." Barney looked over at the dogs then up at the sky. "We'd better hit the trail again. I want to reach Morrison's place before dark. It's not too far and we'll stay with him and his wife tonight."

"I'd like to hear more about him before I meet him. Does he run a stopping place?"

"No, but I always manage to make his place for one night at least on my trips through here. He enjoys it and so do I. If you're with me you'll be welcome." Barney smiled as he continued: "The latch is never on the door in this country. Haven't you heard of northern hospitality? But we'd better get moving." He stood up.

Charlie walked beside his companion and watching the

dogs as they pulled the loaded sled, admired their cared-for appearance. He noticed that some were mixed breeds and different from their leader, which was a husky and looked like a wolf. He said thoughtfully, "Mail must be mighty important to these people living so far from civilization. They must be lonely and find it hard to wait months for it. They're winter-bound later on when snow and slides cover the trail, aren't they?"

"Yes, but they have to get used to all conditions if they're going to live up here," replied Barney.

"By the way, what about Morrison, the remittance man, you've aroused my interest in him. Aren't you going to tell me more about him? I'd like to hear his story and the going will be easier listening to a good yarn. I'm still not used to walking all day. It takes a lot out of a city man."

"You've done all right, I admire the way you've kept up with me. Sure, I'll tell you about Morrison." He glanced quickly at the dogs then, satisfied that harnesses were not twisted and that they were behaving well, he began his story.

"Of course he changed his name when he came here, never used his real one. He got into trouble in England and had to leave his home; something to do with gambling. His father had a title, estates and money. Morrison being the younger son wouldn't inherit these so, as is the custom, he went into the army, into what they call a 'line regiment'. That is one in which the officers must come of a very good family. It also means that when a man is in disgrace it goes harder with him. Morrison found this out when he was cashiered from his regiment. His father shipped him out to Canada, arranged for a remittance to be sent him monthly . . . then forgot him.

"I met him when I first came here and he was on the skids then all right. He spent every cent of his monthly checks on booze. Sometimes these were late and arrived three or four at a time. He'd really go on a bender then and sober up only when he was dead broke."

"It's the familiar story of the remittance man on the prairies," Charlie broke in.

"Perhaps the beginning is the same but not the rest." Barney was annoyed by the interruption, but continued: "Although he seemed bent on self-destruction, he was like-able when sober . . . which was seldom. The white folks around here got tired of him and disgusted too. He drifted in with the Indians until even they got sick of him. He was in bad shape the day I brought him a letter from England. He was living in a dirty shack and wasn't too glad to see me." Barney smiled wryly. "He didn't bother to get up off his bunk, just waved his hand towards the stove and told me to make tea for myself as he took the letter I handed him. There wasn't anything to eat in the place, I wondered when he'd eaten last, or how anyone could eat in all that filth.

"He sat up suddenly, staring at the open letter, and muttered,

'They've cut me off . . . who am I now . . . not even what you people have called me . . . a remittance man.' He rubbed his hand over his unshaven face then sat staring at the floor.

"I felt sorry for him but knew there was nothing I could do, so I left. No more mail came for him so I didn't see him, though I heard about him once or twice. It seemed that he was in a worse condition than ever.

"One day a year later I had a big surprise. I met him on the trail and wouldn't have known him if he hadn't called out to me. He looked fine. He was in good physical shape and there was a quiet dignity in the way he spoke. He didn't

beat about the bush, but said he'd come to his senses and
was living a good life now. Told me he'd married and was
happy. Said he had a trap-line, doing all right with it, too.
I didn't know till later that he'd married an Indian girl. I
found that out when I brought him the second letter from
England.

"They were living in a comfortable cabin by the lake. She
was a fine girl, tall and graceful, quiet-mannered. These
interior Indians are better-looking, I always say, than the
coast ones. She had their home fixed up real nice, neat as
a pin, and the supper she served was a real good one. You
could see how he felt about her and he treated her with
respect. He was contented and happy."

"I gather he had stopped drinking," observed Charlie.

"Indeed yes. He told me he was getting good prices for
his furs and getting them regularly to the Hudson's Bay
post."

"What was in the letter you brought him," Charlie broke
in impatiently.

"He didn't say. Just looked it over quickly and when
he finished reading it put it into his pocket and went right
on talking. She looked at him curiously but didn't say anything about it."

"Did you ever find out what was in it?" asked Charlie.

"Yes, but not for some time. I left the next morning and
a lot happened before I saw either of them again. One day I
was on the dock in Hazelton watching the sternwheeler arrive
with passengers from the south. A man standing by himself caught my attention. By the way he was dressed I could
tell he was an Englishman and new to the north. I forgot
about him and was surprised that afternoon when the hotel-
keeper stopped me as I was leaving his hotel. He introduced
me to the Englishman and asked me if I'd take him out to

Morrison's place. He had come all this way to see him. I was going near there with some supplies, but doubted if this chap could make the trip. I suggested that I drop in and ask Morrison to come into Hazelton. He agreed when I told him how rough the trip would be for him.

"When I gave Morrison the chap's message he seemed to know why he had come, wasn't a bit surprised, and agreed to meet him in Hazelton. I left and when I got back to town a week or so later, heard the news. Everyone was talking about it; Morrison had gone south on the boat with the stranger. I sifted all the stories and rumours I heard and one fact was clear. He'd left his wife and gone back to England."

"He'd deserted her after all she did for him?" Charlie interrupted.

"That's what it looked like. I heard also what was in the second letter I'd delivered to him and that he hadn't read in front of his wife and me. It was from a firm of solicitors in England and told of the death in an accident of his father and only brother. You know how fact can be stranger than fiction . . . well, he was the only one left to inherit that title and the estate in England."

"Why didn't he take his wife back with him to share his good fortune? She'd shared the rotten breaks with him. Was he ashamed of her?" asked Charlie.

"That is what everyone around here said and the women were pretty mad about the whole thing. Some said mighty bitter things about him. They all felt sorry for her. We only saw her once when she came into town after he'd been gone a month. She walked into the telegraph office, asked if there was a wire for her, then didn't speak when the operator said 'No'; just hurried away. You could tell she was too proud to want our sympathy. Guess she thought we pitied her and wanted to be left alone.

"I thought a lot about her that winter and got to worrying about how she was getting on, so I made a trip out to see her. She was living alone; had refused to go back and live with her people. She came to the door but didn't ask me to come in, just listened quietly to me. She said there was nothing she needed and thanked me. I didn't know when I felt so low as I did looking at her, sad and alone, yet still proud. You bet I cursed Morrison as I left her but she didn't know that. You could tell she was strong the way she looked at you."

"Did anyone ever hear from him?" interrupted Charlie.

"I was coming to that. Two months later I was down again watching the river boat tie up at the wharf and, glancing at the passengers, I got a shock. I looked again and sure enough there stood Morrison at the rail. He waved and called to me but I turned away. I had no use for the man and did not want to see him. But he didn't wait to speak to anyone, just rushed off the boat and up to the livery stable. I saw him riding out of town like a streak of lightning. Everyone was talking about it that night. Next day I began to feel differently about him and I guess I was plain curious, so went out to see him and find out things for myself."

"Did he go straight to his cabin?" asked Charlie.

"You bet he did. When I got there he opened the door, and what a greeting he gave me!" Barney looked into space for a moment. "I can see them like it was yesterday. She smiled at me in that shy way of hers and when I went in, I could feel happiness right there in that room. They both insisted I stay the night and you should have tasted the supper she gave us. Afterwards, we sat by the fire and talked, rather he told me what happened. She sat silent, just content to watch him.

"He had decided what he had to do when he went back to England with that stranger. There was no use taking his wife because he figured he'd only be gone a month or so, then back home with everything fixed up for good. But he made the big mistake of not telling her this. He knew his cousins and an old aunt who ran the family, would look down on her because she was an Indian. He wasn't taking her over there to be hurt. He knew too that she'd never like living in England. He didn't want to live there either. So he got the idea of turning the title and estate over to a cousin. He did not realize what a long time it would take to do this. He smiled when he told me about the scene with his haughty old aunt. She insisted he give up the idea, marry an English girl and settle down to what she claimed was his duty to his family. But he said he finally made her understand that he would never do this and that he thought as much of his wife as he could have of any English girl. She also realized that he looked on B.C. as his home."

"Did he ever go back?" asked Charlie.

"Not even for a visit. He bought a pack-train and did well with it. Later he bought a ranch and they're settled in that now and live well. She's been a good wife and happier than most women I've seen. You'll see what I mean when you meet them tonight." Barney stopped speaking, his story ended.

There was beauty in the white stillness about them and in the snow-clad hills. There was a majesty in the freedom of this country which pressed back all sense of civilization, thought Charlie as he looked about him. He thought of Morrison in this deep silence.

"I think I understand why he could never again settle

into a conventional life in England," he said. "He carved a new life out of this wilderness, his mistakes behind him. Maybe there are more remittance men than we know who have been trying to do the same thing."

"Perhaps a great many, and we have not understood them," replied Barney.

The two men were silent as they tramped on into the gathering dusk.

Up The Stikine River By Sternwheeler

Memories of a Trip into the Wilderness of Northern B. C.

I was as excited as any girl of twelve years would be the day we started up the Stikine River in a sternwheeler. When we left the small town of Wrangell, Alaska, behind us that summer morning I realized though we were a long way from my home in Vancouver. We still had a long way to go before we reached our destination, Telegraph Creek.

I stood at the rail and watched the large paddle wheel at the stern go round and round, churning the water to a white foam as it propelled our long, flat-bottomed boat. It looked like a giant crab trying to waddle through the water. Everyone on the wharf at Wrangell waved and shouted goodbye as the shrill, tooting whistle sounded above their voices. I looked about me and saw the two small decks, one above the other. The top one seemed to lean against the high, thin smoke stack which was belching black smoke at a terrible rate. I thought the boat looked very nice, though a bit clumsy. Clumsy, it might be, it was more comfortable and modern, I was told, than those which ran on the rivers in earlier times.

I had been surprised to find that I was the only one of my sex making the trip to Telegraph Creek, but I soon realized the advantage of this. The men passengers and crew showed that they intended to make my time pass pleasantly and do their best to spoil me. My father who was taking me with him on this holiday jaunt relaxed his discipline to the minimum, even regarding bed-time hours.

Our captain was a sea-faring man and very kind-hearted. He set some of the crew to making a deck game for me to play should I become lonely. He said it was to be a surprise. It was. It turned out to be a game rather like pitching horseshoes. I must say my father and the other men certainly enjoyed it immensely, so I seldom had a chance to play.

The river fascinated me. I didn't want to leave the deck that first day. The banks on either side were heavily timbered and huge trees stretched out at us as we passed. Snow-capped mountains in the distance reached silently towards the sky. There was not a single settlement along that river. The telegraph line was the only link with civilization. The lonely silence was eerie.

I was thinking of this when one of the passengers came to ask me if I would care to go below and see his foxes. It seemed that he was going to Telegraph Creek to start a fox farm. This amused our captain who said:

"Talk about taking coals to Newcastle. Why, the barking of wild foxes in the hills will keep you awake every night when you get to Telegraph."

I was delighted with the soft, furry animals in their cages in the hold of the boat. A little red one attracted me and I slipped my finger through the wire as he pressed against it. He looked so innocent and shy, yet quick as a wink his little paw shot out and scratched my finger. I backed away and after that watched from a distance. The fox-farmer said he was going to breed and cross them. It was a long time before I understood that he meant he was going to make money mixing breeds for colour and variety and selling their pelts. Years later I met him again and learned that he had done very well. He had shipped blue, silver and cross-foxes to Prince Edward Island where his father had a fox farm.

That evening we pulled into the bank and the boat slowed to a stop. I asked someone if we had reached Telegraph Creek so soon. The men laughed when they heard my question and one of them pointed to a huge wood-pile lying near the water's edge. He explained that we were going to tie up for the night and the crew would "wood-up." Puzzled, I hurried to find my father and ask what that meant. He explained that sternwheelers had wood-burning fire-boxes and the more wood that was thrown into them the greater speed was made by the boat. I hurried back to the rail to watch the wood-passers throw long slabs aboard. Others of the crew started to cut them up and then piled the wood for the next day's use. This routine was repeated nightly during the trip.

After dinner we went ashore for a walk. The path was just a rough trail running along the river bank. I felt again the eerie silence and the strangeness of being cut off from the world. We were the only human beings in all that primitive wilderness. Looking up I saw the telegraph line and noticed what looked to me like small glass cups on the poles. My father laughed when I asked about them. He said they were more useful than glass drinking cups would be in those woods. They were insulators. Every one must be unbroken or the telegraph service would be disrupted. He went on to explain how linemen had to travel for weeks through the rough, lonely country, making sure that the telegraph line was in good condition.

One of the passengers joined us and told some interesting things about the days when the Indians cut trails like the one we were following, using them to "line their canoes." He explained that "lining" meant dragging a boat along by a rope. A steersman and paddler or two stayed in the boat to guide it while others walked along the trail by the shore. They pulled the rope over their shoulders and so towed the boat by "line." They did this when rapids or water too swift to navigate made it necessary. The sternwheelers were "lined" in the same way through some parts of the river.

When we returned to our boat I was glad to find a supper laid out in the dining saloon. I was terribly hungry and had to be reminded to wash my hands. The Captain was already at the table and in a jolly mood. My first experience with his habit of teasing came when I was reaching for a second helping of cold roast beef. He looked in my direction and said,

"It's going to be mighty hard on the hungry people in Telegraph Creek if we're held up at the Canyon. The way our meat supply is dwindling we'll have to dip into the cargo we're taking them for their winter supply. You know when the river freezes over they don't get any more supplies."

I hurriedly pulled back my hand from the platter, blushing guiltily as I thought of these poor people doing without winter rations because of my greediness. Suddenly one of the men snickered, and the others burst out laughing. Then I realized that it was just one of the captain's jokes.

But our skipper made up for his teasing by telling some very interesting stories about his early experiences on river boats on the Fraser and other rivers. He told us too about the first sternwheeler which was built near a small settlement called Soda Creek in the northern Cariboo. It was called *Enterprise* and started its first run in 1863 from Soda Creek which at that time was the northern terminus of the Cariboo Road. It went on to Quesnel then the beginning of the wagon trail into the goldfields. He had piloted river boats for many years and remembered the days when he had had difficulty in keeping discipline aboard his boat which carried dance-hall girls, gamblers, prospectors and those brave women who followed their husbands to the young country. These people had one purpose in common: the desire to make a fortune or carve a new life in the northland. The dance-hall girls were as well-behaved as any while travelling on his boat, he said. The gamblers were careful to ask the captain's permission before starting a game. He chuckled as he added that they knew that if they misbehaved they would be put ashore with the prospect of finding their own way through the woods to some far-off hamlet, and possibly perishing in the attempt.

A captain must know the river thoroughly and learn to recognize its powerful currents and whirlpools. A challenge lay in the canyons for the one who would risk low water in a dash between towering walls of rock. But the wise captain tied up to a bank until the water rose. Jagged rocks in the rapids often waited to destroy wooden keels. It was necessary also to learn the depth and speed of the water. Sandbars were an ever-present menace in shallow water.

The Captain must have noticed my increasing nervousness as he talked of these dangers which lay ahead of us because he suddenly changed the subject, and father remarked that it was my bed-time.

Certain things stand out in my memory about the next few days. One was the white flag we saw one morning, flying by the river bank. The sternwheeler drew into the shore

and I waited eagerly to see what would happen. The
Captain and some of the crew went ashore and returned
later with an old man. He had a long white beard and his
ragged hair came down to his shoulders. A tattered potato
sack which he had over his head slipped as he was being
helped aboard and I saw a soiled bandage, stained with
blood.

He was a prospector who lived alone in his cabin near
a creek where he panned for gold. He had begun his search
for gold during the Klondike rush and had wandered ever
since through the northland. A true prospector, he still
lived in the hope of finding a new El Dorado and a fortune. A few days before our boat arrived he had had an
accident. He was working a new claim in the hills when a
huge boulder which had become loosened struck him on
the head and knocked him unconscious. He had no way of
knowing how long he lay there. When he regained consciousness he managed to drag himself back to his cabin.
Now he was anxious to get to Telegraph Creek which he
called "the city." As soon as his wounded head had proper
attention he would return to his solitude.

It was amazing to hear him speak in a whisper; his voice
was almost gone from disuse. He had been a hermit so
long he dreaded the noise and confusion even of our small
boat, and was content to spend his time in bed alone during
the long trip. However, he seemed not to mind too much
when I slipped in to see him. I soon learned to understand
his whispery voice when he felt like talking. He told me
about his wife and daughter who had been about my age
when he left them in San Francisco. He had hoped to
make a fortune and return to them. But years had passed.
He had not wanted to write to them until he discovered

gold and now he did not know where they were. His faded
blue eyes brightened hopefully as he whispered,

"Some day soon now, I'll strike it rich and find them."

He seemed to know more about that country than anyone
else. When the boat tied up at the bank one evening he told
us that if we would walk to a nearby stream we would find
the best trout we had ever tasted. The men could barely
wait until dinner was over and, best of all, they allowed me
to go with them. The crew fixed me up with a special tackle
and we started off.

After we arrived at the creek I was told to sit quietly in
a certain spot and drop my line into the water. The men
moved further along the stream. It was a lovely place with
the prettiest rocks and pebbles which I longed to gather. Suddenly I felt a tug and excitedly pulled in a fish. It was not
much bigger than a sardine, and much too small to be hurt.
It was not nice getting it off the hook, but I managed and
decided to take it back and put it in the wash basin in my
cabin with plenty of water for it to swim in. It flopped and
wiggled until I finally got it into my pocket where it settled
down and stopped moving about.

I grew restless and seeing bushes with berries on them,
I started to pick some. The berries smelled nice in the
warm evening air, and I had just eaten a mouthful when
I heard a noise in the bushes. I saw two small eyes peering
out at me. I screamed and ran and didn't stop running or
yelling until I reached the fishermen. They had heard me
and thinking I was hurt, ran to meet me. When I told them
some wild animal was in the bushes they were not alarmed.
They were indeed very much annoyed. It seemed that my
father and another man had dropped everything, including
a fishing pole with a trout on the end of it and the pole had
gone down the stream with the fish. I had upset the fishing

party and was in disgrace. They could not find any trace of an animal and decided I had seen a mouse. I forgot my fish until late that night. Then I smelled it and sneaked out on deck where I tossed the remains overboard.

I still remember how excited I was when we rounded a bend in the river and heard them shout, "Telegraph Creek," the first habitation I had seen since leaving Wrangell. The sternwheeler moved slowly from right to left in the river as the Captain sought the deeper channels in the grey muddy water. I was so busy watching our craft's movements that it was not until someone called my attention to the people standing on the bank that I heard the excited voices shouting: "The boat's coming in." We were then so close to the landing that I could see more people running from the wooden buildings spread along the slope which rose sharply behind the small town. Hills and snow-capped mountains looked down on creeks and valleys running south from the opposite shoreline. Looking at Telegraph Creek with its painted and unpainted wooden buildings, I heard one of the passengers say:

"It's a wonderful thing to think of these people having the courage to live year in and year out in isolation like this."

The houses and cabins seemed huddled together for protection against the vast loneliness of the country. We could hear dogs barking. There seemed to be hundreds of them, huskies and mixed breeds of all sorts. I learned later how necessary dog-teams were for transportation in winter when ice covered the river. I saw Indians, half-breeds and white people, all waiting for us to land as soon as the boat tied up. The men hurried forward to help unload the freight. We were greeted warmly and seemed almost as important as the supplies in the hold. Strangers were always welcome to these people.

I had hardly stepped ashore when my father's friends, who owned the independent trading post and stopping place, insisted that I be their guest. They proved to me that northern hospitality is lavish indeed. As we walked along the boardwalk I saw Indians and half-breeds looking at me with great curiosity. I was just as curious about them and my hostess answered my many questions. She said the Indians were nomads. They travelled about that country hunting and trapping and brought their furs to the trading post.

Later that day I was taken into the trade-room and watched the people who flocked around the counter where the trader and his assistant were sorting the goods our stern-wheeler had brought. I was happy to see that there seemed to be plenty of meat in spite of all I had eaten on the way up the river. The white people were laughing and talking with the passengers while the Indians stood apart, talking in low voices. But all the women, white or dark-skinned, were anxiously scanning lists they held and watching as supplies were placed on the shelves. It was exciting to watch and listen to these people who seemed so natural and free from restraint.

The next day the telegraph operator's wife took me for a walk and showed me the old Hudson's Bay Wagon Road which wound into the hills. We went a short way up the Atlin trail and I was so thrilled I had to stop every few minutes and look about me. We were walking on the very trail used by the early fur-traders and the men who later took that route into the Yukon to beat the hordes who fol-lowed the coast-line in the days of the gold rush. I pictured bands of Indians walking on this very path before the white man came here. I realized how very young our country was. This was the very trail that the old hermit prospector had travelled when he went to the Yukon. He told me about it when I visited him in his cabin on the boat coming up the river. I began to understand why he had built his cabin by a creek in the hills rather than live in a city. My companion showed me the direction taken by the prospectors who trekked from Telegraph Creek to Lake Teslin and on into Dawson.

My companion on this walk went on to say that Telegraph Creek had enjoyed a boom during the gold-rush days. The Hudson's Bay trading post had been quite important at that time.

Recently the Cassiar country, had become known throughout the world for its big game.

Specimens of grizzly bears, mountain sheep and goats and other animals shot here, were on display in European museums. This had renewed the importance of Telegraph Creek. Wealthy hunters flocked into the village to complete their outfits and to pick up Indian guides.

Among these hunters had been some from Germany, Austria and Hungary; many of them were titled men.

When World War I broke out, quite a few were in this area. They slipped down the Stikine River into Alaska and so through the then neutral U.S.A. back to join their regiments in their native countries.

Our stay in Telegraph Creek was all too short to suit me and the day soon arrived when we started down the river for home. The only adventure I had until we reached the Canyon was the battle of the mosquitos. It was impossible to out-wit those hungry insects who tried to get ahead of me when I jumped into bed with the mosquito netting tucked about me. The ones who were shut out buzzed angrily, while the winners bit me. Next morning when I told about my almost sleepless night the Captain laughed and suggested a remedy. It was bear's grease. I refused to rub myself with that evil smelling stuff, and kept on battling my tormentors.

There had been many references made to "shooting the canyon" and I was nervous as we neared it. Would the Captain make a dash through if the water was low, or wait until it rose before we went through? In Telegraph Creek they had said that the water was going down fast.

One nice thing about our skipper was his sense of duty to his ship. When we arrived above the canyon he said the water was too low for us to chance the passage. We would wait outside for it to rise.

We were on deck that morning when I heard the putt-putt of a gas-boat and rushed to the rail to see it. I was soon joined by the other passengers. As it drew near, we saw that its sole occupant was a young man. He waved a careless greeting and chugged over to pass close to us. We were all wondering who this wanderer of the wilds might be when the booming voice of our skipper reached us. His question, 'Where do you think you're going?" echoed over the narrowing channel betweeen the boats. The shouted repy left us all gasping,

"I'm headed for Telegraph Creek. Must get this load of dynamite up there quick."

Again the Captain's voice boomed out, this time in seaman's language, as he ordered "the young fool" to keep away from us.

There was no reply from the gas-boat as its owner, grinning up at the alarmed faces lining our deck rail, continued in his course in our direction. I was about to run to my father for protection when the small boat swung over and passed within a few yards of us. A sigh of relief went up from our passengers. Everyone thought the danger was over

—then it happened. The steady chug of the little engine died into a choking sputter and stopped. Instantly the current caught the little craft and whirled it about. Before we knew it, the dynamite-laden boat was heading straight towards us.

The awed silence was broken by the roar of the Captain's voice as he shouted his orders. Men with boat-hooks stood ready to ward off the death-dealing vessel. One of the crew held a coil of rope in his hand. Meantime the young man had deserted his tiller and worked franctically with his dead engine.

I felt faint with fear as my father put his arm around me. As I turned to hide my face in his shoulder I saw the gas-boat caught by an eddy in the current and shot further into the stream. It was not going to hit us after all. However, the danger was not over until the young man had caught the line thrown to him and snubbed it around a thwart. The dangerous little craft was at last brought to rest on the bank at our stern.

My father hurried me below to my cabin. He had seen a red-faced skipper stalking towards the stern of our steamer to interview the unwelcome visitor. It was no place for a lady, young or old.

The next day the river had risen enough for us to go through the canyon. The water rushed madly through the narrow passage. Beside the steep cliffs on either side were eddies and whirlpools. The water breaking against rocks sounded in places like thunder. The swirling foam from the paddle-wheel at the stern threw spray into the air until the sun's rays caught it and turned it into sparkling jewels.

It was not long after this when we again saw Wrangell and were back in Alaska, the Stikine River behind us.

Home in Vancouver after a quick trip down the coast,

I learned that the Port Simpson, the sternwheeler I had travelled on, was soon to be taken off the river for good. The river boats had replaced the Indian canoes and crude rafts of explorers, voyageurs and pioneers of our rivers. When the sternwheelers were gone another era in the history of our Province would be ended.

Back in school, I found my lessons in Canadian history more meaningful as a result of my trip up the Stikine River. The colourful stories of the early days of our Province became very real to me.